THE VOICE

OTHER WORKS BY THE EDITOR

No Need to Stammer   *Methuen**
Your Speaking Voice and its Possibilities *Muller**
Your Stammer and How to Correct it   *Muller*
Clear Speech for Stage, Platform and Pulpit *Muller*
Speech Training for Children   *Muller*
Speech Training, its Science and Art   *Methuen*
The Stammerer's Choice   *Methuen*

* Out of print.

THE VOICE

An Introduction to
Practical Phonology

BY

W. A. AIKIN, M.D.

NEW EDITION BY

H. St. JOHN RUMSEY, M.A.

*Late Choral Scholar at King's College, Cambridge
Consulting Speech Therapist at
Guys Hospital*

LONGMANS, GREEN AND CO
LONDON • NEW YORK • TORONTO

LONGMANS, GREEN AND CO LTD
6 & 7 CLIFFORD STREET LONDON W1

ALSO AT MELBOURNE AND CAPE TOWN

LONGMANS, GREEN AND CO INC
55 FIFTH AVENUE NEW YORK 3

LONGMANS, GREEN AND CO
215 VICTORIA STREET TORONTO 1

ORIENT LONGMANS LTD
BOMBAY CALCUTTA MADRAS

New Edition 1951

PRINTED IN GREAT BRITAIN
SPOTTISWOODE, BALLANTYNE AND CO. LTD.
COLCHESTER AND LONDON

PREFACE TO THE 1951 EDITION

To be invited to revise such a valuable book as this is a great compliment and to undertake such a task is to accept a very great responsibility. The knowledge that Dr. Aikin and I were in full agreement in all essentials and that he had expressed his approval of my books and theories now makes me willing to bring 'The Voice' back into the hands of those who seek a thorough working knowledge of phonology and the phonetics of Standard English.

In my revision I have confined my efforts to the introductory section which constitutes an explanation of the rest of the book, and here I have added fuller explanations and illustrations only where Dr. Aikin's meaning was a little obscure. I have possessed my own copy of this book for more than thirty years and I have read and re-read it more than any other book on my shelves.

I conclude with the hope that as Dr. Aikin, who studied medicine at Guy's Hospital, gave one generation of readers such valuable help, so may I, who had the honour to serve the same hospital for nearly a quarter of a century, hand on this great book to a new generation of readers, who will, I hope, find in its pages an interest and inspiration as great as I have done.

H. ST. JOHN RUMSEY.

161 CLARENCE GATE GARDENS,
LONDON, N.W. 1.

PREFACE

SINCE my publication of 'The Voice : Its Physiology and Cultivation,' in 1900, considerable advances have been made both in the subject and in the means of applying the principles then brought forward.

In bringing out a new edition it has become necessary to remodel and rewrite the whole work, and to regard it as an introduction to the practical science of Phonology·

The present work is addressed principally to those whose profession it is to train the speaking or singing voice, and therefore certain scientific and technical matters are dealt with somewhat minutely. But I hope that it may also indicate to men of science what the real problems of voice training are, and how much may be done by them in the promotion and demonstration of Phonological Principles.

There is a large field open in the analysis of vocal sound, and I regard the few observations which I have been able to make as only sufficient to demonstrate the physical system upon which the vocal functions are performed. In making practical use of these materials, as far as they go, I do not propose a special 'method' of teaching, but the foundation for all methods, which scientific truth is alone capable of establishing.

W. A. AIKIN.

LONDON, 1910.

CONTENTS

CONTENTS

LIST OF ILLUSTRATIONS

THE VOICE

INTRODUCTION

PHONOLOGY is the science of vocal sound. It is based upon the physical laws involved in the production of sound, and upon the physiological laws which govern the functions and actions of the living organs of the voice. In its widest sense it should include the study of all animal voices, but in this volume it is confined to the human organs which enable us to speak and to sing.

The main object of specialising this science is to gather together all that is known about vocal sound and capable of being demonstrated, so that it may be brought into much closer contact with technical requirements than has hitherto been practicable.

While bringing before those engaged in physics and physiology the vocal problems which are in need of further research, it places at the disposal of those who are responsible for vocal teaching the definite principles upon which vocal development must be conducted.

Phonology, however, always remains an integral part of the general sciences whence it springs, and cannot be separated off as far as knowledge is concerned; but in practice it builds its independence upon a wider and more intimate acquaintance with vocal requirements. It is by studying the sounds of language and music that we learn what is demanded of those organs with whose natural functions we are directly concerned. But it should be clearly understood that phonology is only specialised by the inclusion of these additional branches of study. Its true authority in vocal matters is derived entirely from the physical and physiological principles which form its foundation. However complete a knowledge of phonetics, elocution or music may be, it can only approach the voice from an outside point of view. The real principles of voice training have to be applied from within, and must be based upon the phonological laws which govern the sounding properties of the organs themselves.

In assuming general responsibility for voice training, phonology is doing no more than is claimed by common sense in the case of every other function of the human body.

The case of the voice, however, differs in one particular from others. Its use in organised speech is a faculty acquired entirely by education.

It is quite justifiable to say that defects in the speaking voice can only be due to (1) organic causes— e.g. malformations, etc.; (2) neglect of errors that might have been corrected; or (3) direct misinstruction. Of these the first cause is very rare in comparison with the others, and the educational obligation is therefore obvious. In all matters of public health true scientific principles have to be carefully applied, and in the department of public education it is not possible to neglect the phonological principles upon which the faculty of speech must be developed in the schools.

It is not necessary to point out any further the importance of a real knowledge of the voice in all branches of oral education, and it has become imperative that a properly founded scientific basis should be established in order to provide teachers of all kinds with both certainty and uniformity in their methods.

The study of phonetics cannot be regarded as sufficient for the needs of the voice. The investigation of the sounds of speech and their reference to a phonetic alphabet no doubt greatly facilitate the correct pronunciation of languages, but they cannot reach any of the problems which underlie the actual development of the voice as a natural sounding instrument.

Phonetic and phonological inquiry actually meet in the sounds of language, but while the former fixes the sound by comparing it with others of a similar nature, it is left to the latter to determine its constitution as a sound, and to show how the organs produce it. In phonology we have first to take the accepted phonetic form of any sound of speech, and then we have not only to observe the action of the organs that make it, but to satisfy ourselves that the principles of sound, and the natural behaviour of the organs, are properly applied to it. We go so far as to indicate how a particular sound should be produced when we are able to show at the same time the phonological reason for it. In fact,

every item of phonological teaching must be justified
by some particular advantage to the organs themselves
and to the sounds they produce.

The general principles of the voice are now quite
sufficiently well known to enable us to make definite
suggestions as to the use of the organs in speaking and
singing. As to the principles themselves, there is very
little that is not understood about them ; but in their
application to vocal sound, owing to the difficulties of
examining and analysing the natural actions of the
organs, there is still much minute work to be done,
especially in the matter of their proper demonstration.
But as soon as it is realised among educationists that
phonology is in a position to direct them in this difficult
branch of their work, and has even set up a definite
standard of pronunciation for them to refer to, there
will be greater inducement for scientific observers to
take up this line of research.

The position of phonological science with regard to
education is that of a referee. It cannot be expected
that teachers should be phonologists in the full sense,
for they could not all possess sufficient knowledge of
the voice organs to study them minutely. Neverthe-
less, it is impossible to direct the development of those
organs with certainty by any method that is purely
empirical, and since a rational basis actually exists, it
can only be to the advantage of teachers to understand
at least what phonological principles are, and how they
are applied to the organs with which they have so
much to do.

The practical object of phonology is to provide

teachers with the knowledge to enable them to understand the vocal principles they are to apply in their teaching of language, speech, and song.

The linguist, elocutionist, and musician can no longer be accepted as authorities upon vocal science. The phonologist must, therefore, be ready to accept the responsibility of that position, and also to acquaint himself with the practical details of phonetics, declamation, and music, so that he may be able to understand what the teachers really want to know, as well as the difficulties with which they have to contend. It is not necessary or even advisable that he should carry on the practical work of voice training himself, except in so far as may be necessary in the training colleges and musical institutions, where the teachers to whom public education is entrusted should be thoroughly equipped and qualified to follow their important professions.

THE VOICE IN GENERAL

THE study of speech is necessarily complicated because it involves the thorough understanding of a triple mechanism, the component parts of which must be perfectly co-ordinated if the best results are to be obtained. The subject is the more elusive because many of the best speakers know nothing of what will be found in this and the following sections. This is because during the years of childhood they have gradually learned to speak by imitation and so the complicated process of speech has become automatic, they would therefore gain little, if indeed any, advantage by the study of this book ; for all, however, who aspire to teach it is essential thoroughly to grasp the principles of speech individually and collectively.

This section and the full understanding of it provides the key to the understanding of the whole book, and while every effort has been made to explain speech mechanism in simple words readers are advised to study this section carefully, and, if necessary, to read and re-read it before passing on to the following sections.

In order to understand what the voice is, it will first be necessary to regard it in its purely physical form. There is no artificial instrument made in exact imitation of the human voice, but a single reed-pipe of a church organ is the nearest approach to it in principle, and will serve as illustration of its general structure. That arrangement consists of—

(1) A wind chest, into which air is pumped by bellows.

(2) A vibrator or reed, which produces vibrations, and is the source of sound.

(3) A resonance chamber or resonator, which modifies that sound by giving to it additional qualities.

The air pumped into the wind-chest is trying to escape—that is, it is under compression. Its only outlet is through the narrow slit at the free edge of an elastic plate, forming what is known as a vibrator or 'reed.' The force of the escape causes this reed to oscillate in such a manner that its fine slit is repeatedly opened and closed, and the air passes out in a rapid succession of minute puffs, and transmits to the surrounding air a regular series of undulations or sound waves of a uniform frequency. The sound is thus produced by the physical action of an elastic vibrator. But above the vibrator there is an air-chamber or resonator with solid walls, which through its property of resonation, favours within it those vibrations which are adaptable to the dimensions of its hollow interior, and the vibrations of the 'reed' are thereby re-arranged before they reach the outer air. *Those that suit the resonator are reinforced, and those that do not are antagonised or suppressed.* In the reed-organ pipe under our consideration, the note of the vibrator and the resonant note of the resonator are carefully tuned to suit one another.

The sentence above printed in italics requires a special explanation, and in order to understand the full implications of the words—*suit*—and—*antagonised*, we must set down some basic facts about the mathematical aspects of —*pitch* (or to use its scientific name *frequency*) and *resonances* (or to use their musical equivalents—*harmonics, overtones* or *partials*).

TABLE OF FREQUENCIES AND HARMONICS

32		is the frequency of C′ the BASIC NOTE				
32 × 2 = 64	,,	,,	,, C	,,	1st Overtone	
32 × 3 = 96	,,	,,	,, G	,,	2nd	,,
32 × 4 = 128	,,	,,	,, c	,,	3rd	,,
32 × 5 = 160	,,	,,	,, e	,,	4th	,,
32 × 6 = 192	,,	,,	,, g	,,	5th	,,
32 × 7 = 224	,,	,,	,, ?	,,	6th	,,
32 × 8 = 256	,,	,,	,, c′	,,	7th	,,
32 × 9 = 288	,,	,,	,, ?	,,	8th	,,
32 × 10 = 320	,,	,,	,, e′	,,	9th	,,
32 × 11 = 352	,,	,,	,, ?	,,	10th	,,
32 × 12 = 384	,,	,,	,, g′	,,	11th	,,
32 × 13 = 416	,,	,,	,, ?	,,	12th	,,
32 × 14 = 448	,,	,,	,, ?	,,	13th	,,
32 × 15 = 480	,,	,,	,, ?	,,	14th	,,
32 × 16 = 512	,,	,,	,, c″	,,	15th	,,

As will be seen in the table, the pitch of a note is expressed scientifically as a ' frequency.' To take an example, the frequency of ' Middle C ' (the nearest ' C ' to the lock of the piano case) is—256.

Two scientific facts will make the laws of frequencies and overtones clear.

(1) To raise the pitch of any given note by an octave is to double its frequency, so :—

NOTE	C'	C	c	c'	c''	c'''
FREQUENCY	32	64	128	256	512	1024

(2) The frequencies of all the harmonics of any given note are multiples of the frequency of the original note.

On a previous page (7) we read—' Those resonances that do not suit the resonator are antagonised or suppressed.' In the table we see that overtones 6, 8, 10, 12, 13 and 14 are marked with a note of interrogation ; that is because these overtones do not coincide with any notes on the piano, so that they could not harmonise with the basic note, but would contribute discords. For this reason a piano is so constructed that the hammer hits the wire at a point calculated to break the sequence of harmonics at the sixth. To continue the harmonics would produce what might be called—*a musical smudge.*

As is mentioned on a later page several wind instruments such as the flute, oboe and clarionet work on a different principle. Whereas in the case of the string instruments the note of the vibrator predominates and is merely enriched in quality by the harmonics, in the case of these wind instruments the harmonics usurp the pitch of the note of the vibrator, so that the pitch of the note heard is that of the harmonic, which completely absorbs and smothers the original note (of the vibrator) which evoked and created the harmonic.

These and many other facts about sound are fully explained in books about music, and although they are interesting they will not help us to an understanding of the contributions made by the vibrator and resonator and their co-ordination, so we pass on to a further consideration of the human voice.

The analogy between this mechanism and that of the human voice may now be traced as far as it is applicable. The lungs form the wind chest. Air is drawn in and pressed out again in the process of ordinary breathing. To produce sound, the outward passage of the air is obstructed by drawing across the windpipe two elastic membranes—the vocal cords—which form the ' vibrator ' or ' reed ' of our vocal mechanism. The immediate consequence of this action is that the elastic edges of the vocal cords oscillate, and a regular series of undulations is produced in the air by the rhythmically interrupted escape of air under pressure, and sound is emitted.

Our analogy holds good so far. The force of air in the wind-chest of an organ acts upon the ' reed ' in exactly the same way as the force of breathing out acts upon the vocal cords. But we possess the additional power to vary the force of the breath, and to control the rate of the vibration of the cords, thereby giving to the vocal note a wide range of intensity and pitch, that is not found in any artificial instrument.

To understand further the mechanism of the human voice we must realise that the note formed by the vibratory action of the vocal cords *is never heard*, because this sound can reach the outer air only by passing through the throat, mouth and nose, which individually and collectively form the resonator. Here, therefore, the process is similar in principle to what we have already noted with regard to an organ pipe.

In the case of the human voice, the sound becomes modified and receives certain qualities of tone and character according to the resonating properties of those hollow spaces, of the throat, mouth and nose, as determined by their size and shape. The power to change to some extent the *size*, and to a greater extent, the *shape* of the human resonator, gives to the voice its variations in tone and the numerous characteristic qualities which constitute language.

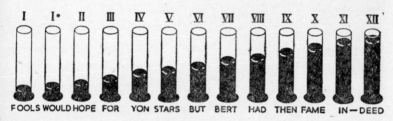

I I· II III IV V VI VII VIII IX X XI XII

FOOLS WOULD HOPE FOR YON STARS BUT BERT HAD THEN FAME IN—DEED

Fig. A.

The character and function of a resonator and the behaviour of vibrating columns of air are but little understood except by a few students of science and advanced students of music, but as it is impossible to acquire a comprehensive knowledge of phonology or phonetics unless the part played by the resonator is fully understood, we will begin with the consideration of a simple fact familiar to us all.

If we fill a jug with water from a tap we know *by sound* when to turn the water off. This is because the water falling into a column of air sets up a vibration appropriate to that column of air. As the level of the water rises, the column of air shortens and a rising scale of resonances is heard—Par, Per, Pay, Pip, Pee, and we turn the tap off knowing *by sound* that the jug is full.

In the above diagram cylinders V–XII represent a rising major scale of resonances, while cylinders V–I represent a descending musical fifth. The sentence written below the cylinders contains the thirteen Simple Vowels as heard in Standard English.

Just as the space in the jug or cylinder is decreased by the rising water, so the air space in the mouth is decreased by the gradual raising of the tongue, shown in Figs. 4 (p. 46) and 6 (p. 56) or it can be increased by the gradual protrusion of the lips as is shown in Fig. 5 (p. 53). From a musical standpoint these added resonances in the mouth provide variations of character and quality, known as overtones, harmonics or partials, while in the sphere of phonetics they provide the Standard English Vowel Sounds.

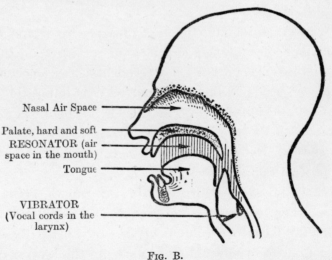

Nasal Air Space

Palate, hard and soft
RESONATOR (air
space in the mouth)
Tongue

VIBRATOR
(Vocal cords in the
larynx)

FIG. B.

To avoid any possibility of misunderstanding the sketch above shows the relative positions of the larynx (the vibrator) in which the voice is produced, and the mouth (the resonator) in which the vowel sounds are formed. The mouth as a resonator is assisted by throat and nasal cavities; details of this are given on pp. 42–57.

The stationary artificial instrument in the church organ represents only one position of the resonator and a single note on the vibrator, whereas in the voice we possess not only a breath force governed by the will and capable of delicate variation, but also a vibrator performing notes of varied intensity (loudness) and extending to a compass of about two octaves or more and an expanding and contracting resonator enriching the sound and introducing into it, by its great mobility and variation of shape, all the characters of human speech. Thus the average larynx provides a compass of two octaves (or twenty-five notes if we include semitones) while the mouth can form thirteen vowel sounds; we see then that the human voice can produce twenty-five notes, each with thirteen different resonances, or (reversed) can form thirteen different vowels on twenty-five different musical notes, so that the full complement is $25 \times 13 = 325$.

There are several wind instruments such as the flute, oboe, clarionet, etc., the pitch of whose notes is produced by strong resonation controlling the vibrations of a feeble reed, but in the human voice the reed is strong and the resonator comparatively weak, so that the vibrations of the reed (the larynx) always determine the pitch of the vocal note, while to the resonator (the air cavity of the mouth) is left the power of augmenting its harmonics only; so whatever changes take place in the mouth, they do not influence the *pitch* of the note, but only its *quality*.

The true conception of the voice is therefore simplified by the recognition of two definite instruments formed on distinct acoustic principles, and performing separate functions, but still absolutely united into one organic whole ; we may therefore divide the study of the voice into the separate consideration of—

(1) The Breath Force,
(2) The Vibrator or Vocal Cords,
(3) The Resonator,

before they are put together in their complete combination.

At the very outset of our study we are met by an important fact, which we are bound to incorporate in the foundations of anything we may think or do in connection with the voice. It is that the vocal cords are mechanically unconscious in the performance of their function. They are not guided directly by the will, but indirectly by our mental perception of the sound they make. We perceive a note in the mind, and produce it by an unconscious mechanism. Children born without proper sound-perception are unable to produce any sound at all, as is the case with deaf-mutes ; for whatever sounds they may be taught later, in order to make their voices audible, the natural function of the vocal cords is never properly awakened. People who have no ear for music are defective in their perceptive faculty, and therefore cannot sing in tune, and it is impossible to find any mechanical means of putting the instrument right ; so that we are bound to admit that we possess no direct control over this instrument, and that we can only assist its development by practising the mental perceptions, and giving them every opportunity to express themselves naturally in sound.

With regard to the other factors in the voice, especially for singing, the breath force must always be directly conscious, for it is that consciousness which establishes control over the whole performance of the voice.

The resonator also, which introduces into the sound of the voice all the characters of language, is conscious in the first instance, but becomes only half conscious by the force of acquired habit.

This is not the place for discussing how far the almost unconscious imitative instinct directs the organs when learning to speak in childhood, but it is quite certain that the conscious control of the speech organs themselves is an important factor in learning to pronounce a foreign language, and in all forms of adult voice improvement. Therefore the resonator must be regarded as the instrument which most depends upon education, and the object of the teacher's particular care.

The cultivation of the voice thus resolves itself into a threefold process, to be undertaken in the following order :—

(1) The development of the capacity and conscious control of the breath.

(2) The conscious establishment of well-arranged positions and movements of the resonator which are to become half-conscious habits of speech.

(3) The free and unhampered use of the vocal vibrator in its natural relation to mental sound-perception and under the dominion of the breath.

(1) The breath, which is the foundation of the voice, naturally comes first, so that its capacity and the control of its output may be cultivated independently.

(2) That the resonator should follow next is because the behaviour of the speech organs (the resonator) can be most clearly understood and securely guided in the whispering voice—that is, when acted upon by the breath only without any vocal note. In this way the principles of resonation are developed on their own merits.

(3) Finally, the process is completed by introducing the natural action of the vibratory instrument in conjunction with the breath, guided, in the case of singing, by the highly cultivated sound-perceptions of the art of music.

Such is the phonological course of events in the cultivation of the voice, and it certainly shows how much more the process is regulated by physical and physiological considerations, than by any knowledge of the arts of elocution or music.

This remark should be understood not so much as a condemnation of existing unqualified conditions of the voice-training profession, but as an encouragement to all those who are thus occupied to realise the phonological needs of their situation, and to make themselves masters of scientific facts with a view to bringing stability and uniformity into their work.

Phonological investigation shows more and more clearly that the cultivation of the breath and of the resonator constitutes an essential factor of physical voice training. Indeed, it may be said to be the main factor of it, since all that concerns the vocal cords belongs partly to an automatic process, in which the general development of musical perceptions and their unconscious reproductions are important factors.

It should not be thought that this conviction was arrived at from the side of phonological science alone. A former leading English teacher of singing, William Shakespeare, in his ' The Art of Singing,' quoted from his own teacher, Lamperti, a saying attributed to Pacchierotti, the great singer of the eighteenth century, which is absolutely in agreement with phonological theories ; ' Chi sa parlare e respirare, sa cantare.' ' He who knows how to speak and to breathe, knows how to sing,' is a statement which confirms in a striking manner the view that a great part of voice training is the cultivation of the breath and the resonator, and that much of the rest can be left to the practice of natural facilities in the expression of musical art.

This saying of Pacchierotti's not only supports our own scientific conclusions, but also gives us good ground for thinking that the old Italian method of singing, which has been regarded as lost, is not lost at all, but has only been misunderstood. It must be remembered that Pacchierotti was speaking to Italians, who enjoyed in his day a practical monopoly of singing. It would be readily admitted that an Italian, having learned how to make the most of the sounds of his mother-tongue, and how to augment and control the forces of his breath, would be in the best condition to use his voice in the service of song. But it does not follow, whatever the vocal beauties of the Italian language may be, that anyone who is not an Italian might acquire the same facilities by trying to sing in that language. Italians make a great deal of the sounds of their words, and it is very rare to find a foreigner who speaks or sings them correctly with natural ease. Indeed, the same thing may be said of all languages, and it might take the greater part of a lifetime to make any language in which you were not brought up, so much your own as to become your natural means of expression ; and in the end there would probably be imperfections in its pronunciation which would not escape the ears of those to whom the language was native. This, then, would throw some doubt upon the possibility of using any language other than your own mother-tongue as the foundation of an art which must be free and spontaneous like that of singing. Therefore the saying of Pacchierotti must not be interpreted in the sense that if you learn to breathe and to speak Italian (imperfectly) you will know how to sing ; but it supports a much deeper and more widely applicable principle—namely, that if you can breathe and speak your own native language, with the same appreciation of sound that the Italians showed in their own speech, you may consider yourself well equipped for the higher flight, if your musical faculty will take you thither.

This is certainly the true application of Pacchierotti's principle, and whether we call it the old Italian tradition or not, the fact remains that if we wish to follow it in this country, we shall have to associate with the development of our breathing the best possible form and quality of English speech, in order to procure for whatever natural gift for song we may possess the freedom it demands. The same principle holds good in France, Russia, Germany, or anywhere, and may be regarded as the logical outcome of the best traditions of singing.

It is quite probable that the study of Italian pronunciation, for the very reason that its sounds have been so carefully cherished, can prove very useful in the improvement of speech generally and of vowel-sounds in particular. But the transfer of Italian vowel-sounds into another language should never be allowed, because it would give to that language a foreign accent.

The foreign accent with which many singers sing the English language is due partly to the custom of deliberately teaching them to do this and partly to the imitation of foreign attempts at English vowel pronunciation.

It will serve no useful purpose to dwell too much upon this deplorable tradition, which robs English singing of so much of its excellence, and entirely unfits it for the operatic stage. It will probably disappear as the public and the singers become more conscious of the absurdity of it, and as they realise that the perfect pronunciation of good English is for them the best foundation for their natural vocal development.

There is little doubt but that the Italians have an advantage over us in many ways, because our language has difficulties which theirs has not, but it is an open question whether the French or German languages are any less difficult to those who are brought up in them, than ours is to us.

One thing is certain, namely, that if we learn to speak our own language beautifully, we are in a position to speak other languages also beautifully, because similar phonological principles of speech apply equally well to all.

At the beginning of adult life, before which time it is neither safe nor advisable to train the voice for song, the speech organs have already established for themselves habits which are not easily altered. Forms of pronunciation (the use of the resonator) can be changed and improved with care, but the general habits of the voice are rather more deeply rooted and have become part of the acquired nature of the voice ; their unconsciousness making them so. If, therefore, the voice is to remain natural, its powers of singing must be built upon these, and not on a foreign importation. A method of singing entirely different from the natural habits of speech betrays its manufactured character, and suggests insincerity.

But here a further word of explanation is required, because while it is undoubtedly true that an unnatural voice conveys an impression of insincerity, it is equally clear and of far greater importance to realise that not only is correct use of the resonator, that is, correct formation of the vowels (or phonetics) learned in childhood chiefly by imitation, but that this is equally true of the use of the vibrator (or voice production) so that children whose parents speak with a harsh voice are likely to use their voices in a similar manner. Now this might per-

haps be described as ' natural,' but the fact remains that
for both speech and song the correct use of the vibrator
is needed. If, however, this dangerous word—' natural '
is correctly interpreted it should mean—as nature
intended the larynx to be used, and that is—without
effort. This effortlessness is achieved by relaxing all
the throat and neck muscles that are not contributing to
the production of vocal tone.

To avoid any possibility of a misunderstanding, let
us be quite clear as to the facts. Bad singing may be
caused through bad voice production (misuse of the
larynx) or through bad phonetics (incorrect formation
of the vowels in the mouth). In other words the fault
may be in the vibrator or the resonator or in both. The
former will cause a thin, harsh vocal tone instead of a
full and musical sound ; the latter is the result of keeping
the mouth in a more or less fixed position ; this causes
what may be called the ' universal ' vowel (usually
ER–VII on the scale of resonances). The beauty of the
English vowels lies in their accurate variety.

These considerations should lead to much greater
care being bestowed on the training of the speech organs
of the young. Bad habits, such as glottic shocks and
clenched teeth, are more easily eradicated in early life,
or, better still, they might even remain unsuggested.
Good models of pronunciation from the very first set
their ' hall mark ' upon the whole character of speech ;
this is far more difficult to instil at a later age.

As the perfection of speaking is to precede the development of singing, it is obvious that no distinction
should be made between the two, except in so far as

singing includes the additional performance of a musical phrase. The conditions under which the voice is acting have to be taken into consideration. The ordinary slipshod type of conversational language has no parallel in singing, which is always more or less polished as regards its diction.

The action of the speech organs in singing in a hall or on the stage should be identical with that required for public speaking or dramatic declamation under similar circumstances, and indeed the existence of a singer who is not a speaker ought to be an impossibility. This may seem perhaps to be rather much to say, but there can be no doubt that if our speech organs were properly trained in the first instance in our youth, the whole process of teaching singing would be simplified. In many cases the difficulties with which a singer has to contend are connected more with the resonator than with the vocal cords ; this accounts for the much too common vocal performance in which the notes are quite distinct, but the words are practically unintelligible. This, after all, is the natural result of voice training by musicians who have only music as their qualification for teaching.

As has already been stated, music is the field in which the beauties of the voice are utilised, and in which opportunities are offered for its perfection in the art of expression, but it has no more power to cultivate the voice than a great violinist would have to turn a bad instrument into a good one by constantly playing upon it. Whereas we know quite well that a good mechanic might make the most beautiful violin ever heard, by really understanding its principles. but without ever being able to play a note.   The same is true of the voice, and it would be possible to train up excellent vocal instruments without any reference to music at all. Phonology fully bears out the views of Pacchierotti in maintaining that he who can breathe and speak is more capable of becoming a great singer than the throaty unintelligible person who may know all the Wagner operas by heart.

THE BREATH

It is not necessary to enter into a detailed description of all the muscles involved in the act of respiration. What is much more important to the speaker and singer is the sensation in his own body of a properly managed breath. For vocal purposes a deep breath and a strong control over it are what must be acquired; for not only is it necessary to take in sufficient air to last for a prolonged period, but its exit has to be regulated so that in a long phrase the end may be as well supplied with force as the beginning, and, at any points within it, the appropriate accents may be given their due prominence.

Under ordinary circumstances the breath is taken in easily and then let out quickly, after which follows a pause; but in speaking and singing the reverse is the case, for the breath must be taken in quickly and put out gradually, and there may be no opportunity for a pause before another breath has to be taken. It is also desirable that a considerable reserve of air should always be kept in the lungs, for much of the volume of the voice, as well as the control, is lost when the muscles of the chest are too much relaxed.

Our natural frequency of breathing is about fifteen

times a minute, and in continuous singing and speaking the opportunities of taking breath occur very much less often, and an increased reserve ought to be kept up at the same time. An increased capacity becomes, therefore, a vital necessity, or the speaker or singer would soon be in want of oxygen. It is also a most desirable acquisition for other than vocal purposes, for the benefit to general health of the full expansion of the lungs can hardly be overestimated.

It is best to study respiration in your own body, and to watch and feel carefully the movements which must be cultivated in order to obtain the maximum of breath and control with the minimum of effort.

The lungs are completely enclosed within the ribs, and occupy the whole region of the chest, with the exception of a small compartment in front and to the left, containing the heart, with which we are not concerned. All the lower part of the trunk uncovered by the ribs is the abdomen, containing the digestive organs, which is separated from the chest or thorax by a large muscular membrane, the diaphragm. This partition forms the roof of the abdomen and the floor of the thorax, and bulges upwards into the latter, so that when it is contracted, the floor of the chest is pulled downwards and forwards.

In order to breathe we have to increase the capacity of the chest, and the air rushes in through the nostrils or mouth. There are two ways of doing this. One by raising the ribs, and the other by contracting and drawing down the diaphragm. The first of these expands the chest in its circumference, and the other extends it downwards. Proper physiological breathing is the conjunction of both movements in due proportion.

The upper ribs are not nearly so moveable as the lower

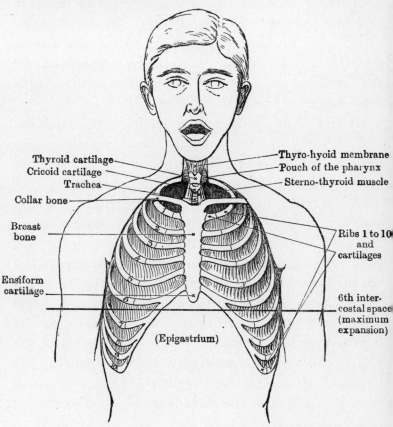

Thyroid cartilage
Cricoid cartilage
Trachea
Collar bone
Breast bone
Ensiform cartilage
(Epigastrium)

Thyro-hyoid membrane
Pouch of the pharynx
Sterno-thyroid muscle
Ribs 1 to 10 and cartilages
6th intercostal space (maximum expansion)

Fig. 1.—Front view of chest with ribs exposed, showing where movement of diaphragm is felt (epigastrium) when ribs are expanded.

ones. In fact, the first and second can only be raised very little, and that by a great effort. The lower ribs, especially those which by means of their long flexible cartilages are attached to the lower end of the breast bone, are much more easily raised, and their action has also more effect, as they correspond to the widest part of the lungs. In tranquil breathing the upper part of

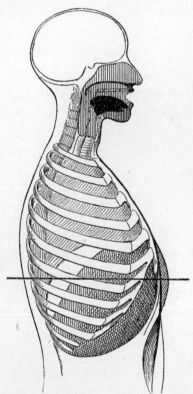

FIG. 2.—Side view of chest and section of resonator in the position of *ah*, showing forward movement of upper part of abdomen (epigastrium) on contraction of diaphragm with raised ribs.

the chest remains almost still, while the lower part expands and the lower end of the breast bone advances. At the same time the diaphragm also descends a little. This is the method adopted in sleep, and is the proper way of obtaining the most air with the least trouble. There is a difference between men and women in this respect, namely, that women use the upper ribs more, and the diaphragm less, than men ; but the rule with regard to singers of both sexes, and all who wish to increase their lung capacity, is the same. This may be stated as follows :—

Cultivate and develop the natural combination of costal and diaphragmatic breathing together, without ever resorting to the extremes of either.

When the lower ribs expand, it becomes possible to contract the diaphragm without causing injurious downward pressure upon the abdominal organs. The increase in the circumference of the chest, due to raising the lower ribs, also increases the circumference of the upper part of the abdomen, and the organs situated there may be pressed forwards by the diaphragm, without causing any distension of the lower part. When the diaphragm descends, the organs which are immediately under it must necessarily also move, as they are for the most part suspended from its under surface ; at the same time, its strong fibres (the pillars) attached to the spine, by their contraction, thrust the organs forwards. This accounts for the bulging of the upper part of the abdomen in proper costal and diaphragmatic breathing, and must be carefully dis- tinguished from excessive ' abdominal ' breathing, which causes distension of the lower part of the abdomen due to pressure upon the intestines from above.

The increased capacity of the lungs to be acquired by the singer must confine itself to the increased expansion of the lower ribs, and the proportionately increased contraction of the diaphragm, in imitation of ordinary physiological breathing, only on a larger scale. This form of breathing is called ' central ' to distinguish it from other forms, such as ' costal,' which is too high, and ' abdominal,' which is too low.

The greatest expansion takes place just below the lower end of the breast bone, and to that spot the attention must be drawn when practising breathing. It is a help to place the hand across the arch formed by the ribs, or rather their cartilages, in front. On breathing deeply the arch widens, and the abdominal wall within it bulges forwards (see Figs. 1 and 2), while the upper part of the chest and shoulders, and the lower part of the abdomen, hardly move.

The best exercises are those which gradually increase the power of the respiratory muscles without straining, and should be slow, even, and rhythmic. As it is essential that respiration should be carried on without interfering with other movements of the body, I would advocate free movement while exercising. It is more likely to make the breathing unconscious, and prevent the stiffness which is so often the singer's ruin both on and off the stage. The simple act of walking supplies a convenient rhythm to regulate the breathing by.

All breathing exercises undertaken for the practice of breathing alone should be through the nose and with the lips closed. At the same time the head and neck are to be held erect and the back straight, but entirely free from any stiffness of the limbs or clenching of the teeth ; it must be possible to move the arms and legs, and even rotate the head if necessary. The eyes should look level and the whole aspect of the face entirely unconcerned, so that if these exercises were carried on at any time before a crowd of people, they could not possibly be detected. It is convenient, at first, to pass a tape round the body at the ' central ' level between the sixth and seventh ribs, which crosses over in front just below the tip of the breast bone. This is the circumference where the most expansion is to take place, and there is to be no raising of the shoulders nor drawing of the ribs up too high, nor is there to be any distension of the lower abdomen below the belt.

Counting either by the swing of the pendulum or steps taken in walking, this central circumference must be expanded slowly from a position of rest, during, let us say, three seconds. The expansion should be maintained for a similar period, and during another three seconds allowed to return to a state of rest. This may then be followed by three seconds' rest. Such a cycle, lasting twelve seconds, requires deep breathing, since it would mean only five breaths per minute—that is, only a third of what occurs in ordinary shallow breathing. If any difficulty is experienced in maintaining this rate of breathing for, let us say, a period of ten minutes, it is advisable to leave out the period of rest and begin a fresh breath immediately after the output.

It is far better for practice to continue a range of breathing which is well within the limits of capacity. On no account are records to be attempted. When three seconds for each part of the cycle have been practised twice daily for ten minutes, and found to be well within the powers of the breather, an advance may be made to four seconds for every part of the cycle, and so on until five, six, seven, or eight seconds are attained. In ordinary brisk walking two steps occupy about a second.

In this form of breathing the whole chest is allowed to expand and return to a position of rest, but great care must be exercised in order to maintain the maximum expansion at the ' central ' level, and to avoid distension below the waistband.

We may now consider how the force acquired by taking a deep breath in the manner described may be best used in the service of the voice.

What we desire is the power of making a clear attack of any strength, of giving any required emphasis, of sustaining and varying at will any length of phrase.

All this will depend upon the control of the forces of breathing out, which regulate the pressure of the air in the chest. We must consider, first, what these forces are before we decide what to do with them.

The lungs are extremely elastic, and when they have been filled with air they are quite ready to expel it again, in the same way that an indiarubber air-ball would do. The elastic recoil of the lungs is, therefore, the first part of the force we employ.

The diaphragm contracts to draw breath in and relaxes to allow the breath to escape again, but it takes no active part in breathing out, except in determining when and how slowly it will cease to contract and yield to opposing forces. These forces are the elastic recoil of the lungs above referred to and the contraction of the abdominal muscles, which, by pressing on the abdominal contents, lift the diaphragm up into the chest from below.

The ribs and their cartilages are also elastic and springy. When the muscles that raise them are relaxed, the principal expiratory force that first comes into action is the elastic recoil of the chest wall itself, as well as of the lungs beneath it. This is followed by the action of the muscles that draw the ribs down and thus further expel the air from the chest.

Thus we may consider **four** forces in the act of breathing out :

(1) Elasticity of lungs
(2) Contraction of abdominal muscles } When the diaphragm relaxes.

(3) Elasticity of chest wall and lungs { When the muscles that raise the ribs relax.

(4) Muscular depression of ribs.

When all these forces act at once the air can be rapidly driven out, as we realise in a deep sigh. But in using the voice we have to learn to control them, so that the air shall pass out with whatever force we elect. If we attempt to control them all at once the process will require most restraint at the beginning, followed by a general relaxation of the chest at the end of a phrase. The principal danger of this would be, that the attack would be liable to be too strong, and the end of the phrase too weak or uncontrolled, which is a very common fault in speaking and singing.

This danger is avoided by learning to use the breath forces one by one.

After a full 'central' breath has been taken the diaphragm may be relaxed alone, so that the first air is driven out by the elastic recoil of the lungs, when the diaphragm is relaxed. This force is strongest when the lungs are fully expanded, and requires no positive muscular effort.

This is followed and supplemented by the contraction of the abdominal muscles, especially those within the arch of the ribs in front—that is, above and not below the waist. By this action the diaphragm may be lifted back to its uncontracted position in the chest, before the ribs are allowed to move. The action of the abdominal muscles may possibly draw the lower ribs down to some extent, but the intention is that the chest should remain expanded until the diaphragm is replaced.

Then follows the relaxation of the ribs, which is felt principally in the region of the lower and most moveable ones, at the side of the chest, which are also drawn down by the abdominal muscles.

Finally, the emptying of the lungs might be completed by the muscular depression of the ribs.

It has been found, however, that when there is a fair lung capacity the final depression of the ribs may be dispensed with, and the elasticity of the lungs, assisted by the abdominal muscles, and some relaxation of the lower ribs, can supply all the force required for the voice, while the ribs remain in a raised position.

The maintenance of raised ribs when using the voice becomes a habit causing no more exertion than simply standing up straight, and it has several important advantages.

It keeps in the lungs a reserve of air which not only

delays want of breath, but by its volume helps to equalise the air pressure, and therefore promotes steady continuity in the vocal note. The increased rigidity of the chest walls also assists in keeping up the pitch of the vocal note. The expansion is always ready to diminish the force of the breath by expanding a little more when very particular control has to be exercised. Another important point is that the expanded chest is associated with the open throat and expanded neck, which gives to the voice its fully rich quality.

This form of breathing is advocated here on the strength of the phonological advantages enumerated, but it is also supported by practical experience. The question of breathing has been the subject of much controversy and misunderstanding, owing in great measure to the use of physiological terms by those who have not fully understood their meaning. But while it must be admitted that some writers have favoured an excessive use of the diaphragm, and others an exclusive use of the ribs, the practice of good singers has been universally to get as much breath as possible by all the means in their power—that is, by a free use of the ribs and diaphragm as prompted by instinct, in spite of what masters may have written.

Good central expansion is quite common among men, both those who have and have not been taught to breathe. But among women there is a natural tendency towards costal or rib breathing, and it is quite common to meet with cases in which the diaphragm is hardly used at all.

It is therefore obvious that, as a rule, men find it

easier to establish their breath control by maintaining an expanded thorax. Their tendency is more likely to be an excessive use of the diaphragm without raising the ribs enough. On the other hand, when women take a deep breath they almost invariably raise the ribs too high, with the result that when a note is attacked the ribs are seen to fall immediately. This is a sign which must always be watched carefully, because it some- times means that the ribs are being relaxed while the diaphragm is still contracted—an action which cannot be too strongly condemned, on account of the undue pressure then exerted upon the abdominal organs.

When the diaphragm is relaxed, while the ribs are held up, the waist measurement becomes less and less. This should always happen, therefore, during the con- tinuation of the sound. The diaphragm yields to the abdominal contraction, and only slight pressure comes upon the abdominal contents. But if the ribs relax before the diaphragm, the whole abdomen bulges down- wards, and if the abdominal muscles also contract, the organs are severely compressed on all sides without any profit to the act of breathing. Any sense of tighten- ing of the belt or waistband while sounding the voice must be immediately corrected, since it is injurious to the health as well as to the vocal sound, as we shall see later on.

When the diaphragm acts only feebly, it requires a considerable amount of time, patience, and practice before sufficient breath can be acquired to allow the costal air to be held in reserve. The falling of the ribs at the moment of the attack is a sign of breath insufficiency, which may be noticed even in some quite successful singers. The early collapse of the chest leads generally to dropping the sound at the end of phrases and gasping for breath in the pauses, two very common defects in both speaking and singing.

The second form of breathing here suggested to be practised is, therefore, that which especially exercises the control over the output of the breath. The chest is to be fully expanded by raising the ribs in such a way that the principal increase takes place at the ' central ' level. When the action is of the ribs alone without the diaphragm, the abdomen falls in so that the clothes and the belt become quite loose. The diaphragm is then allowed to descend until the normal feeling of the belt is restored and no more, and the central diameter increased by some swelling of the extreme upper part of the abdomen within the angle of the ribs in front (epigastrium). Having in this way taken a full breath during a period of three seconds, and having held it for a similar period, the abdominal muscles replace the diaphragm, while the ribs remain expanded and the clothes and the belt become loose again as in the position from which we started. It is well to prolong the last part of this action to, let us say, six seconds. During this exercise the ribs remain unmoved in an expanded position ; the upper part of the abdomen and the lower ribs alone take part in the movement. At the end of breathing out there is considerable depression of the upper part of the abdomen, while the margins of the ribs still project. The maintenance of the expanded ribs requires some little effort from those who are unaccustomed to it, and in the course of five minutes a certain amount of ache will be felt round the chest and under the shoulder blades. This is not injurious, and merely indicates that the bases of the lungs have not habitually enjoyed their full expansion. If the complete cycle first practised should take twelve seconds it may be gradually increased to thirty, but no straining should ever be employed.

This exercise can be modified by omitting the period during which the breath is held, and prolonging the period of output.

The maintenance of an expanded chest in this form of breathing becomes a habit of position rather than part of 'taking a deep breath,' and this is an important point in the idea of breath control. When the ribs are held up by a muscular action not necessarily associated with the feeling of taking a deep breath, the thought of breathing out does not disturb them, and they remain in their raised position independently and not confused with the act of breathing. When practising breathing out, strict attention has to be paid to this, because the raised ribs seem to antagonise the action. In reality they do antagonise the action, with the effect that a large volume of air is held in reserve which need never be used for sounding purposes if the remainder of the expiratory action is sufficiently developed. The element of control which is introduced by this antagonising action of the expanded ribs enables us to regulate the air pressure, during phonation, with great nicety.

Anyone who is about to speak or sing in public would then naturally assume the position of rib expansion beforehand, and maintain it throughout. A warning,

however, must be issued : the shoulders must be
absolutely loose, and the expansion should concern
the level of the sixth and seventh ribs, and not be merely
a thrusting forward of the upper part of the chest. In
men the sensation is that of an expansion just above
the pockets of the waistcoat ; in women the position
is that which frees the body from the tightness of the
waistband. In all cases the expansion takes place
laterally as much as forwards. In practising breathing
there must be as little noise as possible—that is to say,
the whole extent of the air passages must be free from
any kind of contraction or obstruction. The breath
must never be held by any stoppage of the throat. This
device is detected by the slight click which would occur
on releasing the breath.

It is often instructive to measure the breath capacity
by means of a ' spirometer,' but a master who is practically engaged with voices has plenty of opportunities of
noticing by other means when that factor is deficient.
But shortness of breath in phrasing may also be due
to not using the breath sufficiently, or to wasting it,
and it is well to find out by definite measurement if
such is the case.

The apparatus in the form of a ' gasometer ' is the
most accurate. All the rotating machines are subject
to error.

An apparatus has been constructed, called a ' spiro-
dynameter,' which indicates the force used in the
breath within the ordinary limits of the voice. It
consists of a long glass vessel of water, measured by a
scale in inches, in which is suspended by a pulley a

glass tube with a **T** piece at the top.   Through a mouth-

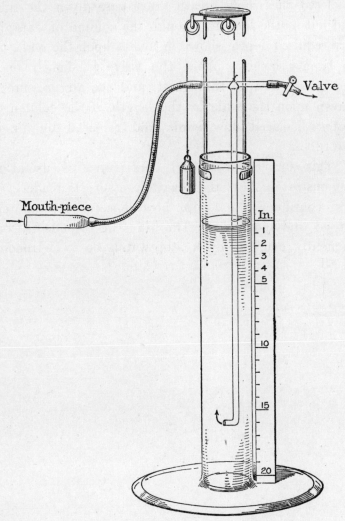

FIG. 3.—Diagram of spiro-dynameter.

piece and an indiarubber tube the breath is passed to
one arm of the **T**, while to the other arm is fixed a valve

D

which can be regulated by a screw. When the valve is closed the whole breath must pass down the tube and out at the bottom through the column of water at any required depth, shown in inches upon the scale, up to twenty inches. When the valve is slightly open the breath escapes through it, and the air pressure is shown upon the scale by the length of the column of water displaced downwards and replaced by air in the tube.

This simple mechanical contrivance is useful in demonstrating how the breath pressure is made even and continuous, and also how it can be accurately varied and controlled. The time in seconds is conveniently counted by a stop-watch or a metronome at 60.

THE RESONATOR

BETWEEN the vocal cords and the lips and nostrils there are certain hollow passages which, by reason of their property of resonation, exert a strong influence upon the sound which passes through them. These hollow spaces form for us a resonator, which stands in precisely the same relation to the vocal cords as the resonator of a reed-pipe does to its reed or vibrator.

We shall examine it here by itself—that is, in its independent capacity as a resonator, without any source of vibration being introduced other than a simple stream of breath.

With regard to resonation in general, it will be enough for our present purposes to know that every hollow space has two main features—size and shape. The size has a definite relation to the length of the sound-wave or vibration that will oscillate within it, and therefore fixes, in a general sense, the pitch of the particular note suited to it, which is called the primary resonant note. The shape by a more complex influence determines the character or composition of the resonant note.

All such hollow resonators must necessarily be in communication with the air, and another factor affecting both the pitch and character of the resonant note is the number and size of the openings.

In every resonator, then, we have to consider these points : the size and shape of the hollow space within it, and the size and shape of its openings.

In the human body the resonator, consisting of the hollow spaces contained in the neck, mouth, and nose, varies in size according to individual build, and is, as a rule, larger in men than in women, and in children smaller than in either. Among adults of the same sex the differences are not very great, but that between the sexes is generally marked.

The shape of the resonator is roughly the same in all human beings, and its orifices are in proportion.

In my description of the resonator I do not wish to go into anatomical details more than I can help. A closer study of the anatomy should be sought in the general text-books.

The general cavity of the neck is formed principally by the pharynx, the lower front portion being occupied by the larynx, which contains the vocal cords. The shape is somewhat like a bag, i.e. wide below, where it includes the larynx, the pharyngeal space behind it, and two pear-shaped pouches on either side, and narrow above, where it is reduced by the tonsils and the base of the tongue to an oval opening into the mouth.

Having been vertical in the neck the resonator becomes horizontal in the mouth, its direction bending at a right angle round the base of the tongue towards the lips. Directly above the pharyngeal opening is the passage to the nose guarded by the soft palate.

The size and shape of the mouth cavity depends chiefly upon the position of the jaw and tongue. When the jaw is moderately open, and the tongue lying flat within the boundary of the lower teeth, it is somewhat hemispherical, expanding considerably into the cheeks and arch of the hard palate, and contracting again towards the lips.

The nose communicates with the back of the mouth by a broad flat opening between the soft palate and the bones of the skull. It is a tent-shaped cavity divided into two by a vertical partition, and opening in front at the nostrils.

The nose is not capable of any change of shape, being composed principally of bone, and should be regarded as an accessory resonator, the influence of which is made prominent only occasionally.

The resonator proper is thus composed of two principal hollow spaces, one in the neck and one in the mouth, communicating with one another through an oval opening between the tonsils and behind the base of the tongue.

The cavity in the neck is capable of a certain amount of enlargement downwards, by drawing upon the larynx from below by the action of the sterno-thyroid muscles. The same action also draws the larynx forwards, so that the pharyngeal space behind it and the pear-shaped pouches on each side of it are enlarged.

This action is quite distinct from that of the sterno-hyoid muscles, which draw down the base of the tongue and press down the larynx from above.

The sterno-thyroids do not pull upon the base of

the tongue until the membrane (thyro-hyoid) between
the thyroid cartilage and hyoid bone has been fully
stretched, and thus a considerable amount of expansion
of the lower part of the resonator is affected without
hampering the freedom of the base of the tongue. It
must, however, be remembered that this muscular action
is not altogether a conscious one which can be directed
by an ordinary effort of the will, but it is intimately
associated with the sense of expansion in the chest,
and becomes as such a permanent factor in the general
position of the resonator, when the maximum of resonation is required.

The cavity of the mouth or upper portion of the
resonator acts under very different conditions.

The lips, the tip of the tongue, and the jaw are
directly subject to the will, and can be placed and moved
with accuracy in whatever way we wish.

The extreme mobility of these organs, and the rapid
manner in which the mouth cavity can be altered by
their action, naturally brings the function of articulation into this region.

Therefore, in order to study and examine any position
of the mouth cavity, it is all the more necessary to
definitely state what the positions of these organs are
to be before proceeding with the investigation, as
otherwise we should not be entitled to speak of any
particular shape of the mouth cavity itself.

It has been acknowledged by all physiologists that
the position of the resonator in the pronunciation of the
vowel-sound *ah* should be regarded as the starting-
point whence all the positions of other vowels may be

said to be differentiated. In the vowel *ah* the whole resonator is in a comfortable open position, but in order to be scientifically accurate it is necessary to define as closely as possible the positions of all organs which take part in its formation. The neglect of this particular precaution has led to an extraordinary amount of disagreement and misunderstanding among those who have investigated this question hitherto.

It should be understood, therefore, that when the sound *ah* is mentioned in these pages the following position of the organs has been prescribed :—

The jaw open so that the front teeth are at least one inch apart.

The tongue flat upon the floor of the mouth, with its tip and margin touching the inner surfaces of the lower teeth.

The lips at rest upon the teeth and not retracted.

The soft palate raised enough to obstruct the passage to the nose.

The head and neck erect and the chest expanded.

The larynx drawn down by the sterno-thyroids (as described above) in association with the expanded chest.

In this position the two principal cavities of the resonator are expanded and open to their full extent without effort, and the breath passes freely out through them without any sound or sense of obstruction. It is principally a position of rest, except as regards the soft palate, which directs the breath through the mouth by closing, or nearly so, the way into the nose. The jaw hangs loosely without any straining, and the tongue lies flat in its forward position without any sense of contraction or pulling, and the lips simply follow the jaw without any action of their own. The erect position of the head, the chest expansion, and the associated action of the sterno-thyroid muscles are grouped

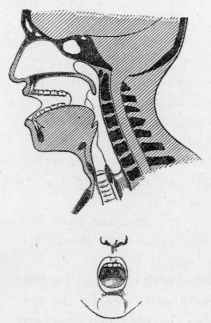

FIG. 4.—Side and front view of the position of the vowel-sound *ah*.

together in the common sensation of wide expansion of the lower part of the neck, which frees the breath from all obstruction there.

In the selection of this position of the vowel-sound *ah* I have been guided not only by the thought of phonological perfection, but also by the experience of a great number of examples, and I believe that it fairly represents a normal and natural sound which would be acceptable to anyone. I must, however, point out that it does not include any forcible depression of the tongue, and my object has been to secure a forward and flat position of the tongue with an open throat and an expanded resonance chamber in the neck, and to prevent the tendency to obtain an increased mouth cavity by tongue depression, on account of the constriction of the throat and the compression of the neck cavity which occur in consequence of that action. The expansion of the neck chamber by drawing down the whole larynx from below by means of the sterno-thyroid muscles and the stretching of the thyro-hyoid membrane, also draws down the base of the tongue to some extent, but that is a very different thing from the depression of the base of the tongue as generally practised without the corresponding expansion of the cavity of the neck. This very technical detail is of great phonological importance, because, as we shall see later, much of the proper action of the resonator depends upon the equality and similarity, or the definite inter-relation, of these two principal cavities, and the expansion of one at the expense of the other is therefore to be discountenanced.

There is also another reason why the base of the tongue should not be hampered by any muscular contraction. The articulation of language depends so much upon the freedom of the body and tip of the tongue that any interference with its mobility is often the cause of indistinct pronunciation. Thus we select the position of *ah* with a view to maintaining equality between the cavities of the mouth and of the neck, and giving the greatest freedom to the movements of the tongue.

The resonant properties of hollow spaces are usually investigated by passing a current of air through them or across them in such a way that the particular sound which is called the resonant note is made audible. The resonant note is the result of the oscillations of the air which take place between the walls of the hollow space, and is therefore most distinct when the walls are regular in form, and it has a pitch in proportion to the size of the space and a character in accordance with its shape. The pitch and quality of the resonant note is also affected by the size and the shape of the orifices.

Speaking, therefore, of resonators in general, it is certain that the resonant notes are lowered in pitch both by enlarging their capacity and by diminishing their orifices, and that their resonant character is altered by varying their shape. It is from this property of varying the character of the resonant notes belonging to the hollow spaces of the resonator that we derive the power of making the vowel-sounds which form the basis of human language. Therefore, if we would understand the true nature of speech, it is our duty to examine these very minutely. The problems involved are undoubtedly complex, but they can be reduced to a sufficiently simple form for the purpose of practical application, and, with that in view, I have designed what is called the Resonator Scale.

The resonant note of the vowel-sound *ah*, forming

the basis of this Resonator Scale, claims our first attention. In the position which I have already defined,
the resonator is double—that is, composed of two
cavities. The shape of the expanded neck, the natural
narrowing in the throat, the hemispherical shape of the
mouth cavity, and their position at right angles to one
another, all tend to divide the resonant vibrations into
two. A phonological proof of this arrangement can be
demonstrated by passing, through the mouth into the
throat, a vibrating tuning-fork, tuned to the same
pitch as the audible resonant note. On arriving at a
spot where the two chambers meet, a strong reinforcement of the sound occurs, which reveals the existence of
what is called a ' nodal point ' or meeting-place of two
systems of vibrations. This ' node ' exists when the cavity
of the neck is expanded and the tongue lies forward in the
mouth, and signifies an agreement between the resonant
properties of the two cavities in that position.

The ordinary way of demonstrating the resonant
note is by breathing out strongly when the organs are
in position. This is in reality a soft form of whispering, without any of that constriction of the throat
which often occurs in the effort to make whispering
more audible. I would remind the reader that when
speaking of whispering it is not intended that there
should be any such constriction of the throat, but that
the sound should be made by the force of the breath
only, with the throat wide open.

Breathing strongly through the prescribed position
of *ah* we shall hear a sound which not only satisfies our
ear as characteristic of the vowel that we know well in

language, but also with a little practice we shall detect a note possessing a distinct pitch.

By an effort of further expanding the chest without disturbing the forward position of the tongue a distinct lowering of the note will be heard. On the other hand, when no definite expansion is exercised the resonant note becomes distinctly higher in pitch. It is in this way that a deeper or lighter quality can be given to a vowel-sound without interfering with the true character of the vowel itself. As in all natural processes it is not advisable to deal with extremes, so we shall consider as the normal resonant note that which is obtained by a fair measure of expansion. Subject to these conditions, it is commonly found that the resonant note of the vowel-sound *ah* has among men the pitch of *c″*, which signifies in music the note on the third space of the treble clef. The power of varying it does not extend to more than a semitone downwards and two or three semitones upwards. Among women, however, whose resonators are naturally smaller, the average pitch of this vowel-sound is usually *e″* flat—that is, about a minor third higher —with similar powers of variation. Among children it is higher still. This is simply due to the fact that the resonant note agrees with the natural size of the resonant spaces.

I regret to be obliged to mention that the great physiologist Helmholtz [1] believed the pitch of this resonant note to be the same ' in men, women, and children.' I can only attribute this error to the use of artificial aids to hearing, and not trusting to the sensitive-

[1] Helmholtz, *Sensations of Tone*, part i. chap. v. p. 7.

ness of the ear alone. I have invariably met with not only the differences between the sexes above described, but also the subtler differences between individuals of the same sex proportionate to the actual measurements of the cavities in their necks and mouths.

Having thus established in each individual this basic resonance of the vowel *ah*, we derive all the other vowel sounds from it by similar actions. These actions

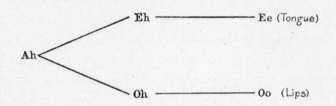

should be divided into two groups, those of changes by the lips, and those of changes by the tongue.

In order to prevent any impairment of the resonation in the mouth we must adopt the open jaw for all vowel positions—that is to say, the changes by the lips and the changes by the tongue are to take place without any movement of the jaw, which remains definitely open to the extent of an inch between the front teeth. This demand may at first sight appear to be excessive, but it is designed with a view to obtaining the maximum of phonological effect without destroying the character of the vowels, in order to show more clearly their true nature as well as to indicate a phonological method of their improvement.

Thus, with the jaw still apart we can differentiate from the position of *ah* three different kinds of *o* and the sound for *oo*, by degrees of closing of the orifice by the lips. The action of closing this orifice has the effect of lowering the resonant pitch of the vowel-sound at each successive stage, and thus five notes of a scale will be heard with *ah* at the top and *oo* a fifth below, and with the three kinds of *o* as in the English words, ' on,' ' or,' ' oh,' upon the three notes between them—

I	II	III	IV	V
oo	oh	or	on	ah
		aw		

The placing of the sound for *oo* at a fifth lower than that for *ah* is not altogether arbitrary. It might be reduced to a lesser interval with a shallower sound, especially when the jaw is partly closed, or it might be carried to a much deeper note by exaggerating the character of the sound. A great number of observations, however, have shown me that most people when passing from *ah* to *oo* by a decided action of the lips, and with the jaws well apart, quite unconsciously make a difference of a fifth in the resonant pitch. The three kinds of *o*, therefore, distribute themselves equally between these two points and occupy the notes of the scale between them. This is readily heard on whispering with a free breath the sounds, *ah, on, or, oh, oo—oo, oh, or, on, ah,* backwards and forwards, if necessary with a piece of card or stick an inch long between the front teeth. As in the case of *ah*, a certain amount of latitude exists for every vowel-sound. The notes of the scale serve merely to indicate good average positions which anyone may practise in order to make these sounds clear in themselves and distinct from one another.

So far I have only spoken of the movement of the lips. There are certain other movements which, although hardly conscious, are of considerable interest in the sounding of these vowels.

In proportion to the closing at the lips there is a

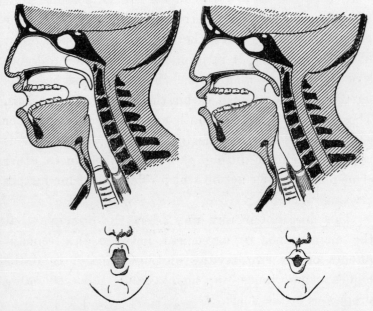

FIG. 5.—Position of the vowel-sound   Position of the vowel-sound *oo*.
          aw (= *or*).

slight raising of the base of the tongue and drawing down of the whole larynx. These actions are practically unconscious and their effect is to enlarge the cavity in the neck and to diminish the opening of the throat, so that we find a lowering of the pitch of the resonance in the neck in unison with that of the mouth. The slight rise of its base, however, should not cause any drawing backwards of the tongue, the tip of which always remains well forward against the back of the lower teeth in all vowel positions.

In speaking of the two resonant cavities we must remember that the resonant vibrations in such a system do not behave exactly as they would if the cavities were separate and independent. It is possible that vibrations could occupy the whole length from the larynx to the lips when the throat is well open. But it is also certain that in proportion to the natural constriction near the middle, the vibrations must be interfered with, and retained within their respective portions. The fact also that the mouth has an opening at either end, and the neck at the top only—for the glottis is considered closed during phonation—introduces other elements into their action which offer a field for further investigation.

This does not in any way affect the principle that the maintenance of agreement between the resonant pitches of the two cavities of the resonator is of the highest importance in maintaining good sounding properties in the voice.

As the actual pitch of these notes differs in different individuals they are numbered with Roman numerals, so that whatever their pitch may be, they always bear the same relation to one another.

Average Man's Resonant Notes :

The next series of vowel-sounds are those which are formed by changes in the position of the tongue. In pronouncing the vowel-sounds contained in the English words—

ah   **up**   her   hat   head   hate   hit   heat

—with the jaw always an inch apart, it will be noticed that the tongue comes forwards and upwards in successive stages, its tip remaining against the lower teeth. In the first three changes, *up, her, hat,* the movement is mostly forwards, but by the time the position of the sound in *head* is reached, the side margins of the tongue are close to the upper molar teeth. In *hate* and *hit* the body of the tongue rises still higher towards the roof of the mouth until it finally reaches its most elevated position in the sound of *heat.*

When these sounds are whispered with a free breath in the manner already described, the gradual rise of the resonance of the mouth is distinctly audible. The pitch of the sound of *heat* being an octave above that of *ah,* the notes obtained for the intervening vowels fall upon the notes of the scale within that octave.

The rise of the resonant pitch of the mouth is, however, not the only change that takes place by the forward and upward movement of the tongue. At every successive step the cavity in the neck is increased, so that we obtain a series of falling resonances in that cavity.

On changing from the position of *ah* to that of *up* the principal movement of the tongue is forwards, and its effect is principally to open the throat. The enlargement of that opening raises the pitch of both cavities

E

of the resonator, so that their unison in *ah* is maintained in *up*, only it is a tone higher.

Further forward movement to the position for *her* establishes, however, a disparity between the two cavities, and we find that while the front resonance of the mouth has risen to a third above that of *ah*, the back resonance of the neck has fallen again to its former level.

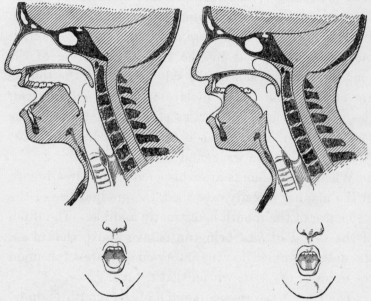

FIG. 6.—Position of the vowel-sound *eh*.   Position of the vowel-sound *ee*.

In the next two positions for *ā* (as in ' hat ') and *ĕ* (as in ' bed ') the front resonance rises and the back resonance falls still further, after which we find that in the position for *eh* it has risen a sixth in front and fallen a third at the back.

In the next two changes the rise and fall of the two chambers become more definite and equal, so that at

the end, in the position for *ee*, while the front resonance
has risen an octave, the back resonance has fallen a
fifth.

This series completes the Resonator Scale, which,
as will be seen in its upper half, becomes a double scale
going in opposite directions, as follows :—

It will be noticed that in the positions of the rather
indefinite and variable vowel-sounds in English, which
occur in the middle of the scale, the resonances are
not perfect in their agreement, which may account for
the many varieties we meet with in their pronunciation.
Two very noteworthy points, however, are shown in
the relation between the two parts of the resonator in
the definite vowel-sounds *eh* and *ee* as in ' hate ' and
' heat.'

In the case of *eh* the resonance of the front cavity
is an octave above that of the back one, and in the case
of *ee* the relation is a twelfth. These relations, har-
monically considered, are as 1 : 2 and 1 : 3 respectively,
and are the simplest that can occur in compound resonation, next to that of unison.

That this relation has something to do with the
natural selection of these sounds *eh* and *ee* as pure
vowel-sounds in all languages, does not admit of any

doubt. In all languages except English they are repre·
sented by the single letters *E* and *I*.

The discovery that these sounds, so universally
adopted in human languages, are those which possess
this particular agreement of resonance chambers, must
also tend to show that the Resonator Scale is not an
entirely arbitrary arrangement, but a key to the method
by which the natural sounding properties of the voice
have been utilised in the service of speech.

Before going further it will be necessary to examine
each of these vowel positions in closer detail.

I. *oo*. The pronunciation of *oo* with the teeth apart
necessitates a forward movement of the lips. In order
that the opening should be round, the corners of the
mouth are drawn forward. The forward position of
the lips slightly increases the resonant capacity of the
mouth. In English we have two sounds of *oo*, as in
' who ' (I) and as in ' wood ' (I*). All that I am prepared to say with regard to the differences between
these two at present, is that the latter is more open than
the former, and that the resonance is of slightly higher
pitch. I have, however, met with instances in which
the second sound has been observed to possess a back
resonance similar to that of the first, but a mouth
resonance a third higher, so that there was an interval
of a third between the two. In any case, there appears
to be an unconscious rearrangement of the base of the
tongue by which the throat is more open for the latter
sound (I*). As a general rule I should be inclined to
regard the position in which both chambers remained
in unison, but of slightly higher pitch owing to the

	I	(I*)	II	III	IV	V	VI	VII	VIII	IX	X	XI	XII
Whispered Sound	o͞o	(o͝o)	oh	o͞r aw	ŏ	ah	ŭ	ēr	ā	ĕ	eh	ĭ	ee
Example:	hoot	(hood)	hope	horn hawk	hot	hard	hut love rough	her bird word burn earth	hat	hen head	hate hail	hit	heat heed

	I	(I*)	II	III	IV	V	VI	VII	VIII	IX	X	XI	XII
Whispered Sound	o͞o	(o͝o)	oh	o͞r aw	ŏ	ah	ŭ	ēr	ā	ĕ	eh	ĭ	ee
Example:	hoot	(hood)	hope	horn hawk	hot	hard	hut love rough	her bird word burn earth	hat	hen head	hate hail	hit	heat heed

opening of the throat, without any other change, as being a better form of resonation than that in which the two cavities became unequal. I would therefore place the second sound (I*) a semitone higher than the first (I), and as a special sound in English.

II. *oh*. In the pronunciation of this vowel we meet with a special difficulty in the English language. Instead of maintaining the *oh* position to the end of the sound, it is a common English habit to move towards the *oo* position—thus, *oh-oo*. This converts the simple *oh* sound into a compound of *oh* and *oo* and is often very marked. Indeed, the sound is so characteristic of English that if it were absent the taint of a foreign accent might be detected ; so that all I would say with regard to it is, that if there must be a suspicion of *oo* at the end of *oh*, let it be as little as possible ; but I must warn those who wish to pronounce this vowel in other languages, that not even a suspicion of the *oo* sound is admissible, and that the pure *oh* without any movement of the resonator must continue to the end in all foreign languages when it occurs. Another common English habit, which is characteristic of the ' Cockney,' is sliding down to the *oh* position from some higher resonance, which may be as high even as IX (= the *ĕ* in ' head ') in its most exaggerated form. This converts it into a compound vowel, and should be discouraged in the interests of pure vowel pronunciation.

III. *or = aw*. This sound, which is the middle one of the three kinds of *o*, is that usually selected for practice, lying halfway between *ah* and *oo*. It is indicated by various letters in English, as in the examples 'paw,' 'pour,' 'pall,' 'Paul,' and in the letter *o* when qualified by *r*, as in 'port.'

IV. ŏ. This, the most open form of the letter *o*, as in the word 'not,' is liable, in American pronunciation, to approach too nearly to the sound of *ah*, which is immediately above it in the scale. According to the scale, the difference of a semitone in resonance is hardly enough ; at the same time the difference of a whole tone might be too much, and bring it too near to the sound of *or*, which is below it. Care must therefore be taken to keep the resonance a large semitone below that of *ah*.

V. *ah*. Since this is the starting-point of the Resonator Scale it is necessary that every individual should know upon what pitch the whole scale is to be founded in his or her particular case. This is a matter for determination. When the breath passes out freely through the resonator in the open position described, there will be but little difficulty in fixing its resonant pitch with the assistance of the pianoforte, and men will usually find it to be *c″* or *c″* sharp, and women *e″* flat or *e″* natural. With the practice of chest and neck expansion, and throat opening, the whole resonator grows larger, and a lower resonance for *ah* will therefore be developed. When this happens it naturally follows that all other vowels, in maintaining the same relation to *ah*, acquire a similar deeper resonation. I would here, however, insist again that no lowering of the resonance of the mouth by depression of the base of the tongue should be permitted. All the expansion of the resonator should be added at its lower end, and the most forward position of the whole tongue carefully maintained, or the proper balance of resonation of the two cavities will be destroyed.

VI. *ŭ*. As already indicated, this position differs from that of *ah* by a slightly more forward tongue and a rounder opening in the throat. It is a sound so common in the English language that it requires careful placing between *ah* and *er*. It represents not only the ordinary vowel-sound in the words ' love,' ' pun,' ' one,' etc., but is often used as a form of unaccented syllable, as in the words ' ălone,' ' tŏ-day,' and in certain terminations, ' temperănce,' ' defendănt,' ' goldĕn,' in which the true vowel-sound has been lost in English speaking.

VII. *er*. This is the sound which seems to depend in English chiefly upon the influence of *r* upon the vowel preceding it, as in such words, ' earth,' ' mirth,' ' worth,' ' purse,' ' herb.'

VIII. *ā*. It will be noticed at once that this sound is nearer to that of *ĕ* above it than to that of *er* below it, and in placing it on the note a fourth above that of *ah* I have rather assumed its lowest possible position. I must therefore warn the student that it may be more convenient to hear this a semitone higher in the mouth— that is, to give it a light and clear character in front, and for its sonority to rely entirely upon good chest expansion beneath it. The deplorable circumstances which have practically banished this characteristic English vowel-sound from the pronunciation of the English singer, are doubtless due to an attempt to give it sonority in the mouth, which of course destroys its vowel character.

IX. *ĕ.* This position is the first of the upper four notes of the scale in which there is a marked rise of the middle of the tongue towards the palate. There is a tendency from here onwards to close the jaw in order to diminish the size of the cavity in the front of the mouth. The more the jaw is kept open the more will the tongue be obliged to come forward, and consequently the more will the resonance chamber in the neck be increased; and, therefore, the better we can conveniently keep our teeth apart, the better will the good resonance of the voice be maintained. This applies especially to the four upper notes of the scale, and offers a phonological reason for pronouncing them with an open jaw. In practising this position (IX) we must be careful that the tongue is sufficiently forward, so that there may be an interval of a sixth between the front and back resonant notes.

X. *eh.* The relation of an octave between the two cavities of the resonator in this position can be demonstrated by placing one finger over the neck and slightly tapping upon it with the other hand. The hollow sound is identified as an octave lower than that which is heard in front by breathing out. Another way of hearing the resonance of the back cavity in your own resonator is by completely stopping the ears. On breathing out while changing from *ah* to *eh*, the back resonance is then heard to fall a third, while the front resonance, with the ears open, is heard to rise a sixth.

XI. *ĭ.* This intermediate position between *eh* and *ee* is so placed in respect of both its cavities, which are thus a tenth apart. It is an important English vowel-sound and must be carefully placed, owing to its frequent use in the compound vowel- ounds.

XII. *ee.* As in the case of *eh*, the fall in resonance of the back chamber on passing from *ah* to *ee* is heard by percussion on the neck, and also by stopping the ears. The rise to an octave above the resonance of *ah* in the front cavity is the highest resonance produced in vowel formation, so that when the jaw is open the tongue reaches its highest and most forward position. At the same time the back resonance reaches the lowest note on the Resonator Scale in falling a fifth.

Thus we find that there are thirteen pure vowel-sounds in English, each with its distinct position and definite relation to the resonance of *ah* upon the Resonator Scale.

These sounds have been called ' pure ' by the grammarians in order to distinguish them from ' impure ' vowels, which have an admixture of other sounds. It is, however, better and more exact to call those that have distinct positions upon the scale by the name of ' simple ' vowels, to distinguish them from the ' compound ' vowels, which require for their performance the passage from one position of the resonator to another.

The compound vowels have a monosyllabic value, and each represents a group of vowel positions, one of which takes the principal accent and the others are to be regarded as approaches to and departures from it, from and to other vowel positions. When the compound vowel-sound has to be prolonged, it is always the principal accented member of the group that is made continuous. In the English language there is a general tendency to make the vowel positions compound by moving the resonator during the sound. Some of these movements have been definitely incorporated in the language, others are obviously faulty, and between the two there are a few which may be regarded as doubtful. We shall first consider those that are accepted as legitimate. They are—

(1) The sounds signified by the letters *u* and *i*.

(2) *ow* and *oi*.

(3) All the compounds of other vowels with the sound of *er*, which has to be considered as a vowel-sound owing to the dropping of the *r*. They are *ear* as in ' hear,' *ere* a in ' here,' *air* as in ' hair,' *ere* as in ' there,' *oor* as in ' poor.'

To these must be added the triple compounds *ire* as in ' hire,' *ure* as in ' pure,' *our* as in ' hour.'

It is also necessary to mention in this connection the sounds of *w* and *y*, which have come to be regarded as consonants, but are in reality vowel positions used often in compounds.

(1) The letter *u* as in ' duke ' is a compound of *ĭ* (XI) with *oo* (I), the accent being on the latter. (' Due,' ' dew,' and ' d'you ' are practically isophonic.)

(N.B. In English compound vowels the *ĭ* (XI) as in ' hit ' is used and not *ee* (XII) as in ' heat.')

The letters *i* and *y* as in ' mind,' ' my,' ' die,' and ' eye ' represent a compound of *ŭ* (VI) and *ĭ* (XI) with the accent on the former. The pure Italian *ai* (=*ah–ee*,

$\widehat{\text{V–XII}}$) is not the same as the English sound. Our first sound has a higher resonance, and more nearly approaches the *ŭ* (VI) in ' much ' than the full *ah* (V) as in ' march.' The second unaccented portion is undoubtedly *ĭ* (XI) as in ' hit ' and not *ee* (XII) as in ' feet.'

(2) *Ow* and *ou* as in ' how ' and ' hound ' are not pronounced in English exactly upon *ah* (V) and *oo* (I). The first sound has a very slightly higher resonance than the true *ah* (V), and the second sound is practically the *oo* (I*) as in ' hood.'

Great care must be exercised in defining this compound on account of the ' Cockney ' dialect, in which the first sound is commonly *ā* (VIII) as in ' hat ' or even *ĕ* (IX) as in ' head.' This disfigurement of its sound must be guarded against, and the resonance of the first sound on no account allowed to be higher than *ŭ* (VI) (similar to *ă* in ' *ă*lone '). In justice to the obvious tendency, it cannot be insisted that the sound is a compound of V–I, although it may be politic to practise this to counteract the ' Cockney ' influence.

Oi and *oy* as in ' hoist ' and ' toy ' are pronounced as *aw* (III) followed by *ĭ* (XI) with the accent on the former.

(3) The sound of *er*, which occurs as the final unaccented part of a large group of compounds, is not exactly the same as the prolonged *er* (VII) as in the words ' her,' ' earth,' ' birth,' etc. It more nearly approaches the lower resonance of *ŭ* (VI) so commonly used in English in all unaccented sounds. Care must be exercised not to allow it to have a resonance any deeper than that, however, for in that case it would

resemble *ah* (V), which corresponds to the drawling affectation not infrequently heard in London.

Then *ear* and *ere* as in ' hear ' and ' here ' are compounds of *ĭ* (XI) as in ' hit ' with *er* (VI*) above described.

(N.B. It should be noted that ' hear ' ($\widehat{XI}$–VI*) is almost the reverse of *I* ($\widehat{VI}$–XI), so that when you whisper ' I hear ' those resonances are heard ($\widehat{VI}$–XI $\widehat{XI}$–VI) going up and coming down upon these two notes of the Resonator Scale.)

Air and *ere* as in ' hair ' and ' there ' denote the position *ā* (VIII) as in ' hat ' followed by *er* (VI*) with the accent on the former.

Oor as in ' poor ' is a compound of *oo* (I*) as in ' hood ' with *er* (VI*). The full *oo* (I) sound in this compound (as in ' pool ') sounds exaggerated.

In the same way *ire* and *our* as in ' hire ' and ' hour ' are triple compounds, in which the first sound VI is accented and followed by a movement up to *ĭ* (XI) and back, and down to *oo* (I*) and back again respectively, that is $\widehat{VI}$–$\widehat{XI}$–VI* for ' hire ' and $\widehat{VI}$–$\widehat{I^*}$–VI for ' hour.'

In *ure* as in ' pure ' the accent falls on the second sound (I*), which is preceded by a movement from the top of the scale, *ĭ* (XI), and followed by another movement to *er* (VI*) in the middle of the scale, thus $\widehat{XI}$–$\widehat{I^*}$–VI*.

It should be remembered that the position of the tongue in the middle of the Resonator Scale is often very difficult to fix, especially when the sounds are not accented. There is no doubt that the accented sounds in such words as ' wonder,' ' thunder,' ' up,' etc., are formed upon No. VI of the scale. But the unaccented

sounds in the words ' alone,' ' upon,' ' to-day,' ' golden '
and words ending in ' -ance,' ' -ence,' ' -ant,' ' -ent,'
' -tion,' ' -an,' ' -ar ' and ' -al ' are not so easy to fix,
but they undoubtedly belong to the near neighbourhood
of the same position. There may be slight differences
in the position of the tongue which alter the sound
without appreciably altering the resonant pitch.

From my own experience of them, I should recommend only a slight leaning in the direction of *ah* (V) or
towards *er* (VII) when the occasion requires it, thus
bringing all the unaccented sounds as near as possible
to the middle note (VI) of the scale.

I have been led to dwell upon this subject because
of the popular fallacy that in good pronunciation we
are expected to revert to the spelling of the word.
Such a course is both pedantic and unnatural, as well
as unnecessary, and is liable to jar upon the ears of
educated people.

Doubtful compound vowels are the characteristic
o, pronounced *oh–oo* (II–I), and *eh*, pronounced *eh–i*
(X–XI), which appear to have taken permanent root in
English pronunciation. They are most noticeable when
English people attempt to speak Italian, where they are
not admissible.

Another is the *our* as in the word ' pour ' and *oor* as
in the word ' floor,' generally pronounced as a simple
sound (III) like ' paw ' and ' flaw,' but sometimes
followed by an unaccented *er* like other compounds of
that nature in which the *r* is not sounded. This is,
however, more a phonetic than a phonological question, and if there are to be distinctions between the

words ' saw,' ' sore,' ' soar,' they may be expressed by
the amount of *er* sound which is to follow the pure
aw (III).

The same difficulty occurs in the discrimination
between the mono- or bi-syllabic nature of—

flour	flower
hire	higher
pure	fewer etc., etc.

Obviously faulty examples of vowel compounding
are met with in the introduction of *er* (VII) or even *ā*
(VIII) before *oh* (II) as in the words ' oh,' ' no,' pronounced *er-oo*, *ner-oo*, and in the substitution for *eh*
(X) in ' may-day ' of the compound *ah-ĭ*, pronounced
' my-dye.'

The compound *ow* (V–I) begun too high as if it were
VIII–I has already been referred to, and belongs to the
same category. The compound *I* (VI–XI) begun too
low as if it were III–XI like *oy* in ' boy,' is another
example of a similar distortion.

These common faults are mentioned here in order
to explain their nature and thereby facilitate their
correction, according to the principles of the Resonator
Scale. It should, however, be insisted that, for phonological reasons, the simple sounds should be preserved
when practicable, and the tendency to compound or
over-compound them should be discouraged as far as
possible, without damaging the natural characteristics
of the best forms of speech.

CONSONANTS

THE consonants represent many varied methods of approaching and departing from the vowel positions. They are produced in a general way by interference with the sounding function of the resonator, that is, they are for the most part constrictions and stoppages of the orifices of the resonator.

They can be divided into two principal classes—

1. Incomplete closures, which are all continuous in their sound, whether 'aspirated' or 'voiced.'
2. Complete closures, which cause sudden explosions opening, or stoppages cutting off the vowel-sounds. They are here classified according to the positions in the resonator where the interferences occur.

(1) The common aspirate *H* is due to the rushing sound of the breath passing through the larynx.

(2) By constriction between the base of the tongue and the palate are made the hard explosive *K* and the sounding explosive *G*, and the continuous nasal *N͡G*.

(3) Between the tip of the tongue and the palate in

front are formed the explosive *T*, the sounding explosive
D, the nasal *N*, the liquid *L*, and the rolling *R*.

TABLE OF CONSONANTS

Where formed	Incomplete Closures				Complete Closures	
	ASPIR-ATES	CONTINUANTS (sounding)			EXPLOSIVES	
		Buccal —non-nasal	Nasal	Tre-mor	Unvoiced (= hard)	Voiced (= soft)
(1) Larynx ..	H	–	–	–	–	–
(2) Tongue (body) and Hard Palate (back) ..	–	–	N͡G	–	K	G
(3) Tongue (tip) and Hard Palate (front) ..	–	L	N	R	T	D
(4) Lips	–	–	M	–	P	B
(5) Lower Lip and Upper Teeth	F	V	–	–	–	–
(6) Tip of Tongue and Upper Teeth	T͡H	T͡H	–	–	–	–
(7) Teeth.. ..	S	Z	–	–	–	–
(8) „ (with lips)	SH	J (soft)	–	–	–	–
	CH = T͡SH	G J = DJ				

Jaw open · Jaw partly open · Jaw closed

(4) At the lips are formed the explosive *P*, the sounding explosive *B*, and the nasal *M*.

(5) Between the lower lip and the upper teeth are
the aspirate *F* and the continuant *V*.

(6) Between the tip of the tongue and the upper teeth are the aspirated and sounded forms of TH.

(7) Between the teeth are the aspirate S and the continuant Z.

(8) Here also, with the assistance of the funnelling of the lips, is the aspirate SH and the continuant J (as in the word 'pleasure'), also the explosive aspirate $CH = \widehat{TSH}$ and its sounding equivalent G (soft) $= DJ$.

On reviewing the consonants from the point of view of the action involved, we find that there are three explosives K, T and P with their corresponding sounding explosives G, D and B which represent the sudden opening of complete closures at different points in the resonator. These are all of momentary duration only. All the other consonants are capable of continuation, and must therefore be regarded as positions of the resonator in varying degrees of incomplete closure.

Thus there are aspirates H, F, TH, S, SH due to rushing of the breath through various partial closures without any vocal note. The light pressure of the tip of the tongue against the upper teeth in TH is usually assisted by the lower teeth, but this is not necessary. Corresponding to the last four of these there are the continuants V, $\widetilde{TH}$, Z, J which are fully vocalised.

The three nasal sounds M, N, and $\widehat{NG}$ are vocalised and continuous, the passage through the mouth being closed at different points and the sound emitted through the nose.

The continuant L is only an obstruction caused by raising the tip of the tongue to behind the front teeth, and is fully vocalised.

The tremor of the tip of the tongue against the hard palate in the front of the mouth which corresponds to the forward pronunciation of *R*, is also vocal and continuous.

As all the vowel-sounds are to be pronounced with an open jaw, and since all the consonants are complete or incomplete closures of the resonator, it follows that when a vowel is preceded by a consonant, a quick and decided opening to its proper resonating position must take place. As far as the jaw is concerned there need be no closure for *H*, *K*, *G* and $\widehat{NG}$, and very little, if any, for those consonants which occupy the tip of the tongue alone, *L*, *N*, *T*, *D*, *R*. Those that occur at the lips, such as *M*, *P*, *B*, do not require the complete closure of the jaw, and the same may be said of the lip-teeth and tongue-teeth consonants, *F*, *V*, *TH* and $\widehat{TH}$. But those that are produced by the teeth, *S*, *Z*, *SH*, *J*, require complete closure of the jaw.

From this it will be seen that on approaching the vowels, considerable movement is necessary for the last group of consonants, but less for those that precede them.

A reverse movement is required for the closure of the various vowel-sounds by the consonants. Considered according to the places where they occur, we may regard the aspirate *H* as the normal opening in the larynx at the cessation of a note. When this aspirate is used as a terminal consonant, it therefore signifies the normal escape of air made inaudible by control of the breath. There is no movement in the resonator, and the cessation of sound in the vowel position is caused by the separation of the vocal cords.

The fully open jaw is maintained on making the closure with the back of the tongue for $\widehat{NG}$, K, and G. When the vocal sound ceases, the breath escapes through the nose after $\widehat{NG}$ and through the mouth after the necessary explosion of K and G.

In the next group, L, N, T, D, R, the jaw remains open, while the tongue applies itself to the front of the palate. In the case of the continuants, after a momentary sounding of the consonant, the sound ceases, and breath escapes, while the tongue is still in position. The escape of breath gives to the explosives their natural character. It is to be carefully remembered that after a terminal consonant there is to be no vocal sound, but only an escape of breath. In the case of R, the roll practically ceases with the cessation of the vocal note, the tongue coming to rest with the breath escape.

The escape after L is on each side of the tongue, while its point is still against the front of the palate.

In N the escape is into the nose.

The explosion in T and D is of the breath only.

The same rule applies to the lips. The breath after M passes through the nose, and the explosion of P and B is caused by the breath that follows the note, in precisely the same way as in the case of $\widehat{NG}$, K and G.

The aspirates F, TH, S and SH occur in the breath after the cessation of the note. Their corresponding continuants, V, TH, Z and J, are caused by the same positions before the sound has ceased. The breath that escapes after they have been momentarily sounded is controlled, while the lips and teeth are in position, so that these continuants are followed by a subdued aspirate made inaudible by breath control, and not by any vocal sound, nor even by any whispered *er* due to departure from the consonant position.

All the terminal consonants come straight into the vowel-sound, and close it without being preceded by any perceptible intermediate sound, due to alteration of the vowel position.

Some consonants especially require care in this respect. The fault often lies in moving the jaw, and in not confining the movement to the tip of the tongue. For instance, the forward *L* in the word ' hill ' comes straight into the vowel-sound *ĭ* (XI), and is not divided from it by any sound such as in ' hi-ull.'

The *R* sound, when it is rolled, is commonly preceded by *er*, which, strictly speaking, should be absent. It is a difficult sound in English mouths and is often replaced by *er* altogether.

Its clearness is, however, only a matter of practice, so long as the tip of the tongue is free and not tied down by the ' frenum ' beneath it. The dropping of *R*, except when followed by a vowel, is practically an ' accepted fact ' in English, and the sound must therefore be treated accordingly.

Compound consonants are chiefly combinations formed by *L* and *R* with another consonant prefixed to them : *PL, BL, FL, SL, CL=KL, GL,* and *TR, DR, PR, BR, FR, CR=KR, GR, THR, SHR.* Another group is that in which *S* is prefixed to various others, as *SN, SM, ST, SP, SC=SK, SQU, SW.* The three explosives *T, P, C=K,* admit of the double combination of a prefixed *S* and a following *R,* as in *STR,*

SPR, SCR, and *L*, as in *SPL* (*vide* Pronunciation Chart).

The action in all cases is that of passing straight from one consonant to the other with nothing between, until the breath is liberated in the continuant or the vowel which follows. For example, in the work ' stroke,' the aspirate *S* is caught upon *T*, which explodes upon the rolling *R*, and then opens quickly, straight on to the vowel *O*, which in its turn is closed by the *K* and explodes on the breath. Only *ro* is vocalised.

A voiced consonant never precedes an aspirate or explosive at the beginning of a word as it might at the end. Nor do we find a sounding consonant following an aspirate or explosive at the end of a word as it might at the beginning.

It is a general phonological principle that during the use of the voice the mouth must be open. All the actual sounding properties of the voice depend upon a free opening for all the vowels, and the mouth is closed only for those consonants which demand it.

In the last column of the foregoing table the position of the jaw is indicated, so that in the last two groups, (7) and (8), a full opening or closing of the jaw before or after a vowel-sound will always be necessary. In the middle group, (4), (5), (6), where the jaw is only partly closed, although the lips may be together, some movement is also required, but not to the same extent. In the first group, (1), (2), (3), it is not uncommon to notice a slight closing of the jaw, especially when the consonant is emphasised, but for the sake of ' economy of force ' it is well to reduce the movement to the least possible, thereby increasing the work which is thrown upon the tongue, which is in reality much more agile than the jaw.

It may seem strange that the pronunciation of N should be recommended with an open jaw, because there is a general tendency to assist the application of the tongue to the roof of the mouth by partly closing it. However common this may be, it is certainly unnecessary, and destroys the resonant property of the mouth. It is quite easy to convert the most forward position of L into N, by simply spreading out the front part of the tongue until it fills the half-circle of the upper teeth, and without altering the open position of the jaw.

The advantage of this lies not only in the fact that the jaw is already in a vowel position, and only requires a movement of the tongue to convert it into such, but also the tongue is then so far forward that the throat remains open and the resonant quality of the N sound is greatly improved. This position serves for the consonant T except that in this case the passage through the nose is stopped by the palate, thus closing the passage of air through the resonator altogether. The explosion of T then occurs by the descent of the tongue to any vowel position. D is the same as T, only the vocal sound begins before the explosion takes place, and not with it. These consonants have sometimes been called ' dental,' but they are quite independent of the existence of the teeth, and if they required a name, would more properly be called ' lingual.'

Some concession must be allowed in the case of the

forward rolling *R*.　It is quite uncommon to find among
English-speaking people that the tip of the tongue is
loose and free enough to perform the roll without partly
closing the jaw.　It is anyhow a question of practice,
and some effort should be made to get it as open as
possible.

Special mention must be made of certain unclassified
consonantal sounds.　*CH* as in the Scotch ' loch ' is an
aspirate formed by an incompletely closed *K*, but since
it is not strictly speaking an English sound, I have not
included it in the list.

Ch in ' church ' is in reality a compound like $\widehat{TSH}$,
but since the *SH* requires the closure of the jaw, the *T*,
which immediately precedes it, is not formed by the tip
of the tongue on the roof of the mouth as is the case
with the ordinary *T*.　The tip of the tongue remains
behind the lower teeth, and the explosion is produced
by the front of the hard palate and the nearest portion
of the tongue that can reach it, while the jaw is already
set for *SH*.

This consonant ranks as a mixed explosive and
aspirate, and has its corresponding ' sounding ' consonant in *DJ*, which is expressed in English by the
soft *G* and *J* in such words as ' George ' and ' Judge.'

The soft *J*, corresponding to the sounding form of the
aspirate *SH*, represents the French *J* as in ' jeune,' but
is heard in English as a form of soft *S* in such words as
' pleasure,' ' confusion,' etc.

What is usually called ' soft G ' is in reality *DJ*, and
this differs from the hard *G*, formed between the body
of the tongue and the back of the palate, by being

transferred as far as possible to the front of the mouth. Part of the similar change which has taken place in transforming the hard $C=K$ as in ' call ' into the soft C as in ' cell ' is due to the same action, namely, bringing the sound to the front of the mouth as well as depriving it of its explosive character.   This has resulted in English and French in the softening of the hard $C=K$ into the simple S ; in Italian it still preserves something of its explosive character in a sort of $\widehat{TSH}$; and in Spanish it has lost the explosive and is aspirated in the same position, like a kind of lisp.

These forward modifications have been designed to suit those vowel-sounds which require the most forward position of the tongue, and are pronounced far forward in the mouth. We have, therefore, a phonological explanation of the softening influence of *eh* and *ee* and their allied vowel-sounds upon the guttural K and G, which has been adopted in all languages of Latin origin. This is an important matter for the consideration of those who wish to introduce into Latin pronunciation the hard guttural Teutonic $C=K$ and G before $E=eh$ and $I=ee$, in place of their traditional softer forms.

The general adoption of a modification in Italy, Spain, Portugal and France might itself have been sufficient reason to maintain it in Latin pronunciation in some form or other. In $U=oo$, $O=oh$, and $A=ah$, when the narrowest part of the resonator is at the base of the tongue, the explosion of the K and G is most naturally made in that neighbourhood; but when, as in *eh* and *ee*, the narrowest part is between the middle of the tongue and the front of the hard palate, the most natural explosive in that situation would be like a *T*, in which the tip of the tongue still remained behind the lower teeth. It is easy to see how this has become the half-explosive Italian sound, the lisping *TH* of the Spaniards, and the more sibilant sound of the French. This phonological fact is strengthened by the historical circumstance that the Latin language has been continued as a practically living language in those countries ever since the beginning of the Christian era.

PRACTICAL DEVELOPMENT OF THE
RESONATOR SCALE

THE practice of the resonator is undertaken entirely in the whispering voice, that is, with a free passage for the breath through an open throat and mouth, and is directed in the first instance to the acquisition of good positions for the vowel-sounds. With these are then associated free and agile movements for the various consonants before and after the vowels, with no other impediment to the continuity of breath than that which they involve.

The general principles which can be applied to vowel positions are—

(1) That the jaw should remain open for all vowel-sounds, thus relying upon the lips and the tongue for the various modifications of their shape.

(2) That all the positions must be definite and capable of being held stationary, that is, they must not be positions to which the organs spring and immediately retire from. (For instance, the *oo* position requires that the

lips shall be held still, no matter what the
breath may be doing, for any length of time.
The same must be said of the tongue in the
extreme *ee* position.)

(3) The normal position of the resonator as a sounding instrument being considered as open, the
consonants, being complete or partial closures
of the resonator at various points, are all
methods of opening or closing the vowel
positions.

(4) The sensation associated with all vowels and
most of the consonants is that they are
formed in the extreme front of the mouth.

Most people, when they first attempt to make good
vowel-sounds, discover that they have not been in the
habit of opening the jaw sufficiently, especially in the
positions *ee* and *oo*, at the two extremes of the Resonator
Scale. Attention, therefore, should first be given to
the position of *ah*, which has already been defined, and
the same opening of the jaw maintained for all the other
vowels.

The open jaw, the unconcerned lips, the forward flat
tongue can be watched in a hand-mirror.

Further back than that, conscious voluntary movements cannot well be directed, and we are obliged to
judge more by indirect means.

If when the tongue is forward there is still some
constriction of the throat, it may be removed by breathing in and out absolutely noiselessly. The soft sound
required in a good whisper is produced by a strong

outbreath, and not by any constriction of the throat. The sensation is then that its sound comes from low down. It is not advisable to direct the attention of the student to the palate. The unconscious way of raising the palate is by realising that no passage of air takes place through the nose, and that it passes out freely through the mouth.

In a properly whispered *ah* the sensation is that the breath is emitted and meets with no interference until it reaches the teeth. It is blown by the force of the breath right into the front of the mouth, and the more the attention of the student is directed to this region, the less likely are unfortunate contractions of the throat to occur.

It should be borne in mind that we are trying to acquire the best sounding *ah* with as little effort as possible. It is, however, necessary that the head and neck should be erect and the chest expanded, as directed in the second form of breathing, that being the most advantageous to resonation. The pronunciation of *ah* as in ' father,' formed in this way, will give a definite resonant note when we breathe out in the manner prescribed. This note must in each case form the basis of the Resonator Scale for that particular person, the average among men being *c″* and *c″* sharp and among women *e″* flat and *e″*.

By breathing out through this position we can tune the resonant pitch a fifth downwards by rounding and bringing forwards the lips without moving the jaw or the tip of the tongue. We obtain in this manner a satisfactory position for *oo*. Arresting the action of the lips halfway between the two, the sound *or=aw* is determined and the full *oh* and the light *ŏ* find their positions below and above it.

With **a** little practice the five notes of the scale will be readily heard in breathing out through the positions :

All that we have to concern ourselves with in practice is that the jaw should remain open and the tongue forward, and that the orifice at the lips should be regulated without hesitation to these five positions. The same breathing conditions apply equally to all. This is what takes place in those vowel-sounds which depend for their character upon the changes at the lips; in the others the lips remain stationary and the changes are effected by the tongue alone.

Returning now to the position of *ah* while maintaining an open jaw, if necessary with a prop of wood an inch long between the teeth, the position for *ee*, with the tip of the tongue behind the lower teeth and the body of the tongue well up towards the front of the roof of the mouth, will be heard to raise the pitch of *ah* up to an octave higher. When the breathing directions are properly followed and the throat remains open, the deep resonance in the neck can be made audible by tapping it lightly with the finger, or pencil, or it is still better heard by the pupil by stopping the ears. While the front resonance goes up an octave the back resonance falls a fifth.

When first dealing with the resonances it not infrequently happens that the *ah* position contains some depression of the base of the tongue, and gives therefore a deeper resonance than is natural to it. This may not

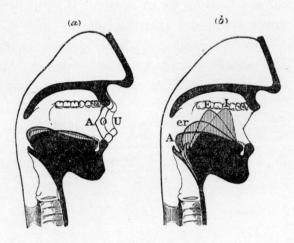

FIG. 7.—(*a*) Relative positions of lips in pronouncing the vowel-sounds A = $\widehat{ah}$, O = $\widehat{aw}$, and U = $\widehat{oo}$.

(*b*) Relative positions of tongue in pronouncing the vowel-sounds A = $\widehat{ah}$, $\widehat{er}$, E = $\widehat{eh}$, and I = $\widehat{ee}$ with an open jaw.

be discovered during the determination of the positions of *oo* and the others lower on the scale, because the unduly enlarged mouth cavity is affected by the lip closing in them all alike. But when the tongue depression is made to give way by the necessity of coming right forward to form the *ee* with an open jaw, the back cavity in the neck may then be found to be smaller than was expected, and the back resonance will not fall so much as a fifth. This indicates that the resonance of *ah* is likely to be naturally higher (*e″* natural if in a woman or *c″* sharp if in a man), and the change can be verified by securing a flatter and more forward position of the tongue and a lighter, unrestrained character in this vowel-sound.

To find the position for *eh* in which the tongue is not so far forward will not then be difficult, and the dull *ĭ* in 'hit,' which is between the two, and the short *ĕ* as in 'head,' which is immediately below *eh*, can be placed so that in breathing through the five positions,

we hear the resonant notes rising first a fifth and then continuing, note by note, the remainder of the scale to the octave.

By tapping on the neck or stopping the ears, there can be demonstrated the corresponding fall in pitch of the back hollow of the resonator down to a fifth below.

The middle portion of the Resonator Scale between *ah* and *ĕ* as in 'head' contains three sounds which are not very satisfactorily resonated, and therefore not so easy to fix upon the scale. When, however, the jaw remains open and the tongue is kept forward in the mouth, the three positions for the sounds, *ŭ* as in 'up,'

er as in ' earth,' and *ā* as in ' hat,' will be found to lie
upon resonant notes within this interval.   The resonant
pitch of the position of *er* is in the middle, that of *up*,
and the sounds allied to it, between *er* and *ah*.   The
pitch of *ā* in ' hat ' is between *er* and *ĕ* (head), but if
anything nearer to the latter. The sound is very variable,
but must be kept within the limits indicated.

Thus we have filled the twelve places upon the
Resonator Scale, starting with No. V and forming the
lower members down to No. I by positions of the lips,
and then starting again with No. V and securing the
upper members up to XII by positions of the tongue.
If there is any tendency to close the jaw, the wooden
prop between the teeth may be used to prevent it until
the necessary free movements of the lips and of the
tongue have been acquired.   Then the prop may be
dispensed with.   (See Table, p. 59.)

If the pupil should be worried by the prop in the
first instance, some consolation may be derived from
the thought that this was probably the device made use
of by Demosthenes, only he is reported to have used a
pebble.

Definite regular practice should be undertaken of
vowel-sounds both alone and in connection with the
various consonants.   For this purpose it is better to take

G

the five principal vowel-sounds—at first with the aspirate *H*—

Hoo   Haw   Hah   Heh   Hee

and practise them in their relation to *Hah*, thus—

Hah-Hoo   Hah-Haw   Hah-Hah   Hah-Heh   Hah-Hee

carefully noting the change in resonant pitch in passing from *Hah* to each in succession.   (Ex. p. 93.)

The transition from the aspirated *Hah* to the un-aspirated *ah* is somewhat subtle in the whispering voice. The difference is not in the strength of the breath only, but the additional sound of *H* is caused by the increased obstruction in the larynx, due to a slight further adduc-tion of the vocal cords, associated with a stronger breath.   In the above exercise there are two aspirates to each breath and a double puff is required, but in

Hah-oo   Hah-aw   Hah-ah   Hah-eh   Hah-ee

the breath is continuous and even, and **Hah-ah** is necessarily one sound.   The unaspirated sounds—

Ah-oo   Ah-aw   Ah-ah   Ah-eh   Ah-ee

may then be practised, great care being taken that no click or ' glottic shock ' is allowed to precede them.   To guard against this prominent evil I prefer to use the *H* in the exercises for common use.

For *H* may then be substituted in turn the following consonants—

L,   N,   T,   D,   R,

which, as they concern the tongue only, require little
or no closure of the jaw.   Then follow those of the lips—

M,   P,   B,

in which the jaw is partly closed for the consonant, but
opens fully again for the vowel.   The tongue remains
at rest with its tip against the lower teeth.   The
lip, tongue, and teeth aspirates—

F,   TH,   S,   SH,   CH,

and their corresponding sounding continuants—

V,   TH,   Z,   (soft) J,   DG,

should follow next, and since they all include some
closure of the jaw they must be followed by a brisk
opening to the vowel position.

I intentionally exclude from the practice the consonants

K,   G,   NG,

since they involve an action at the back of the mouth
which constitutes one of the principal faults in diction
which have to be counteracted.   When the extremely
far forward positions of the other consonants have been
thoroughly acquired they may, however, be practised
with impunity.

The notes of the resonant pitch in the above exercise
descending a fifth, a third, and then ascending a sixth
and an octave make a kind of jingle which is caught by

the ear, and it should be one of the objects of practice to make it as distinct and uniform as possible. For a resonator, which is tuned to *c″* for *ah*, we shall hear—

or if on *e″* flat—

It is necessary to watch carefully the formation of the consonants according to what has already been said in the chapter upon the resonator. The open jaw for the first group is important, because the vowel position is in that respect already prepared, and therefore only an agile movement of the tip of the tongue is required to approach it. The actual position in the consonant *L* differs only from the *ah* position in that the tip of the tongue touches the extreme forward portion of the hard palate where the front teeth are inserted, instead of lying flat behind the lower teeth. The jaw may therefore be left open and the tongue movement practised by itself. When the breath is passed out while the movement is taking place, the whispered sound *Lah* is recognised.

The difference between L and N is that instead of a pointed tongue, the tip is spread out so as to lie flat upon the foremost part of the hard palate. The way through the mouth is thus entirely stopped, and the air passes freely through the nose. There should be no difficulty in performing this consonant without movement of the jaw. The position of T is identical with N, except that the passage to the nose is also closed and a complete stoppage is effected. This is relieved by the sudden descent of the tongue to the vowel position. There is a tendency to assist in emphasising this consonant by raising the jaw.

The position of D is the same as that of T, but the action is less forcible because the explosion caused by the descent of the tongue takes place after the vocal note has already begun. This distinction is quite appreciable in whispering in spite of the absence of the vocal note.

The roll of R without any vocal note is difficult. The definite double ' flick ' of the tip of the tongue on the front of the hard palate is generally audible.

The movement required for opening the lip consonants,

M,   P,   B,

is principally of the jaw. The passage through the nose during M must be carefully watched when opening on to a vowel, and the same applies to the other nasal sound N. In both cases the nasal sound must disappear entirely at the beginning of the vowel-sound.

The definite rushing sounds made by the breath,

F,   TH (hard),   S,

must be capable of being intensified by strengthening
the current of air through them. The upper teeth
must be felt lightly touching the lower lip in *F*, in the
same way as they are felt by the tip of the tongue in
the hard *TH*, and as they are lightly touched by the
lower teeth in *S*. No constriction in the throat or at
the back of the tongue has anything to do with these
consonants or their sounding companions,

V,   TH (soft),   and Z;

the only obstruction to the flow of air is at the
teeth.

It should be borne in mind that the resonant pitch
serves only as a guide. The student should become
familiar with the sense of a well-adjusted position for
ah, and also with the amount of movement required
for his lips to pass to the *oo* position and for his tongue
to reach that for *ee*. This sense of freedom of the
lips, with the tongue well in the front of the mouth,
is what ultimately gives to the speaker the 'natural'
ease of distinctness which is the main object of voice
education.

The following tables of exercises will speak for themselves.

RESONATOR SCALE OF WHISPERED VOWEL-SOUNDS

(Resonant Notes to be suited to the Individual Voice)

I	II	III	IV	V	VI	VII	VIII	IX	X	XI	XII

oo   oh   aw   ŏ   ah   ŭ   er   ā   ĕ   eh   ĭ   ee

Exercise 1.

Whispered sounds only.   A breath for every pair.   Slowly and regularly.

Resonant note	V	I	V	III	V	V	V	X	V	XII
English sound	Hah	Hoo	Hah	Haw	Hah	Hah	Hah	Heh	Hah	Hee
Jaw open	Hah	Loo	Hah	Law	Hah	Lah	Hah	Leh	Hah	Lee
	–	Noo	–	Naw	–	Nah	–	Neh	–	Nee
Tongue tip	–	Too	–	Taw	–	Tah	–	Teh	–	Tee
	–	Doo	–	Daw	–	Dah	–	Deh	–	Dee
	–	Roo	–	Raw	–	Rah	–	Reh	–	Ree
	–	Moo	–	Maw	–	Mah	–	Meh	–	Mee
Lips	–	Poo	–	Paw	–	Pah	–	Peh	–	Pee
	–	Boo	–	Baw	–	Bah	–	Beh	–	Bee
Lip and teeth	–	Foo	–	Faw	–	Fah	–	Feh	–	Fee
	–	Voo	–	Vaw	–	Vah	–	Veh	–	Vee
Tongue and teeth	–	Thoo	–	Thaw	–	Thah	–	Theh	–	Thee
	–	T͡hoo	–	T͡haw	–	T͡hah	–	T͡heh	–	T͡hee
	–	Soo	–	Saw	–	Sah	–	Seh	–	See
Teeth	–	Zoo	–	Zaw	–	Zah	–	Zeh	–	Zee
	–	Shoo	–	Shaw	–	Shah	–	Sheh	–	Shee
	–	Ĵoo	–	Ĵaw	–	Ĵah	–	Ĵeh	–	Ĵee
Base of tongue	–	Koo	–	Kaw	–	Kah	–	Keh	–	Kee
	–	Goo	–	Gaw	–	Gah	–	Geh (hard)	–	Gee (hard)

This Exercise is varied by prefixing any other syllable in place of Hah.

(Whisper only)

Exercises.

2.	V	X	XII	X	V	III	I	III	V
	Hah	Heh	Hee	Heh	Hah	Haw	Hoo	Haw	Hah
as in :	(hard)	(hate)	(heel)	(hate)	(hard)	(horn)	(hoot)	(horn)	(hard)

3.	V	VII	IX	XII	IX	VII	V
	Hah	Her	Hĕ	Hee	Hĕ	Her	Hah
as in :	(hard)	(herd)	(head)	(heed)	(head)	(herd)	(hard)

4.	IV	VI	VIII	XI	VIII	VI	IV
	Hŏ	Hŭ	Hā	Hĭ	Hā	Hŭ	Hŏ
as in :	(hot)	(hut)	(hat)	(hit)	(hat)	(hut)	(hot)

5.	III	V	VII	X	VII	V	III
	Haw	Hah	Her	Heh	Her	Hah	Haw
as in :	(call)	(car)	(curl)	(cake)	(curl)	(car)	(call)

6.	II	IV	VI	IX	VI	IV	II
	Hoh	Hŏ	Hŭ	Hĕ	Hŭ	Hŏ	Hoh
as in :	(hope)	(hot)	(hut)	(head)	(hut)	(hot)	(hope)

7.	I	III	V	VIII	V	III	I
	Hoo	Haw	Hah	Hā	Hah	Haw	Hoo
as in :	(food)	(ford)	(far)	(fad)	(far)	(ford)	(food)

8.	I	II	III	IV	V	VI	VII	VIII	IX	X	XI	XII
	Hoo	Hoh	Haw	Hŏ	Hah	Hŭ	Her	Hā	Hĕ	Heh	Hĭ	Hee

(as in the whole Resonator Scale)

Each preceded in turn by—

L N T D R   M P B   F V   Th T͡h   S Z   Sh Ĵ   CH DG

THE VIBRATOR

THE vibrator or 'reed' formed by the vocal cords is a well-defined mechanism for the production of sound-vibrations in the air. Its action is similar to the 'reed' of an organ pipe in that the elastic tremors of the plates or membranes of which it is composed cause the rapid opening and closing of a minute slit, through which air under pressure escapes in equally rapid minute puffs.

It is not necessary in any practical work upon the voice to go closely into all muscular actions in connection with this mechanism, because they are not directly under the control of the will, and act unconsciously in obedience to mental perception of sound. For this reason the minute study of the larynx itself, in which the vocal cords are situated, will always remain a medical subject connected with physiological and pathological questions. It is not possible to train an organ without understanding something of its action, and a teacher must therefore know accurately what his teaching is endeavouring to produce.

For the individual, the action of the vocal cords can only be perceived indirectly, that is, their action remains unconscious, and the speaker's or singer's consciousness has only to do with the result in the sound which they produce.

At the top of the wind-pipe, through which air is delivered from the lungs, the two membranes called the vocal cords are placed. When a deep breath is taken they fall widely apart so as to offer no obstruction. On breathing out, however, they come slightly together like two draped curtains, one on either side. When we wish to make a sound these two curtains are drawn completely across the tube so as to obstruct the exit of the air. If they were absolutely rigid they would completely stop the breath, but fortunately they are elastic, and, with the act of expiration, the pressure upon the air is able to force its way between the edges of the membranes.

The flutter of the edges is due to their elasticity and is the result of a well-known physical principle which can be studied in the action of an artificial ' reed.' As a result of this, the breath pressure escapes in an extremely rapid succession of small puffs, which produce powerful undulations in the air, and are transmitted in the form of sound. The pressure of the breath is the natural force used in this action, and is therefore directly responsible for the sound of the voice.

The rapidity with which the membranes vibrate is regulated by an unconscious muscular system, which we are able to guide by mental sound-perception, and by no other means.

The fact that those who are born deaf do not know even how to begin to make a sound, although the vocal organs appear to be absolutely normal, is a proof that even the onset of the sound is unconscious. I would therefore protest in the strongest possible terms against any interference with this natural action. The constriction in the larynx, similar to ' a very slight cough,' advocated by a particular school of writers on this subject, is a method which all phonological knowledge must utterly condemn. The complete approximation of the vocal cords, that is, the tight drawing of the two curtains in response to a desire for sound, is in reality only the completion of a natural part of an expiratory act, and, being thus associated with the simultaneous onset of expiratory force, is to be regarded as the simple and natural manner of initiating sound.

This ' glottic shock ' is produced by two muscular folds called the ventricular bands or false vocal cords which, in conjunction with some other muscles, cause a complete constriction of the air passage above the true vocal cords. Their function is to protect the larynx during swallowing and to take any strain exerted by the respiratory muscles during muscular effort, such as vigorous action of the arms or abdominal muscles, involving the fixation of the chest. Their action in coughing is of the nature of a spasm preceding an explosion of the breath as an expulsive effort only, and cannot be accepted as a normal prelude to phonation.

Any action may be admitted into the service of expression, and the ' shock of the glottis ' might possibly be employed when some very marked emphasis is required ; but when persisted in, like all exaggerations, it is the frequent cause of damage to the vocal mechanism,

as well as being quite unnecessary when the proper force
of the voice, namely the breath, is well directed and
controlled.

As I shall have to refer to this matter again later, I
will say no more at present than that the normal natural
onset of a note is an expiratory act, in which the onset
of the breath is simultaneous with the bringing of the
vocal cords into action. When this has taken place
the continuation of the sound is secured by prolonging
the same expiratory act, that is, by maintaining the
force of the breath. The variation of the intensity of
the sound will therefore be regulated by the control
of the breath force. If the breath force should be
suspended, not only will the sound cease, but also the
vocal cords will fall back from their contiguous position,
being no longer held together by the action which is
associated with breathing out. It generally happens,
however, that the note ceases and the vocal cords go
apart before the breath force has been completely
checked. Then there is a slight puff of air emitted
after the note has ceased, which may be regarded as a
normal consequence of the cessation of a note, and can
be reduced to a minimum by careful breath control.
Particular stress is laid upon this point because it lies
at the root of the proper use of the vocal instruments.
The sole responsibility of the breath for the onset, continuity, and cessation of the vocal note is a first principle
of phonology.

The vocal cords or membranes are firmly fixed in
front to the thyroid or shield cartilage at a point where
they touch one another. The outer edge of each is

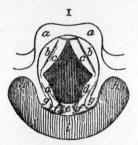

1

Deep inspiration.

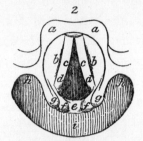

2

Expiration.

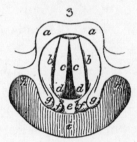

3

Whispering.

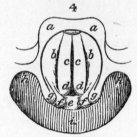

4

A breathy note.

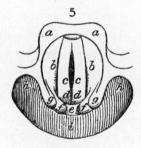

5

A full note.

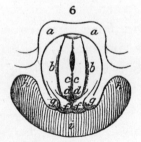

6

A 'compressed' note.

FIG. 8.—Interior of Larynx.

a epiglottis.   *b* false vocal cord = ventricular band.
c true vocal cord.   *d* vocal process of arytænoid cartilage.
e, f, g. cricoid, Santorini, and Wrisberg cartilages.
h pyriform fossa.   *i* pharynx above œsophagus (expanded).

firmly attached to the wall of the larynx ; at the back, however, they are fixed to two moveable cartilages (arytænoid or ' ewer-shaped ') which rotate upon the large cricoid or ring cartilage immediately beneath them, which corresponds to the top of the wind-pipe. The inner edges of the membranes form the slit of the glottis (*rima glottidis*) when they are brought together. The whole of this slit does not take part in the vibration, as the back portion is stiffened by a rod or process (*processus vocalis*) of cartilage projecting from the arytænoid. At the extreme front, where the ends of the vocal cords are inserted, they are prevented from vibrating by touching one another. The true vibrating portion is then that which lies free between this point and the tip of the vocal process. This portion is called the ' pars vocalis ' of the glottis, and that behind it corresponding to the arytænoid cartilages and their vocal processes is the ' pars respiratoria.'

When the cords are brought firmly together the entire force of the breath is expended upon producing the vibration of the ' pars vocalis,' and a firm strong note is the result (Fig. 8, 5).

Should there be an escape between the cartilages of the ' pars respiratoria,' a part of the breath force is wasted and a note is emitted, which is soft and breathy in proportion to the escape (Fig. 8, 4).

While fully recognising the nature and uses of this form of undertone or half-voice, I regard the normal vocal note as meaning the full sound produced by the complete closing of the glottic slit.

The muscular mechanism, which is entirely ruled by

mental perception of sound or ' ear,' acts upon the vocal cords by tightening or relaxing them to quicken or retard their rates of vibration, and so produce notes of higher or lower pitch. Thus every voice can produce notes extending on an average to a range of about two octaves by this locally unconscious means of varying the tension of the vocal cords.

The size of the membranous vibrator differs in different individuals, and thus we have, among men as well as among women, every variety of differently pitched voices between certain limits. The pitch of women's voices is, roughly speaking, an octave higher than that of men's.

The voices of either sex are generally classified, for convenience, as high, low, and middle. The great mass of voices, however, in either case approach the middle variety. Among men the true bass and the true tenor are rare compared with those of the middle type, which, for want of another name, is usually called barytone. Similarly among women the great bulk of voices belong to the middle variety, which may be called mezzo-soprano, although that name has been applied in music to a voice with particular capabilities, and the high soprano and the true contralto are comparatively rare forms of voice.

In dealing with the compass of notes which can be commanded by any particular voice, we can therefore assume that there is a central note in every voice, whence, by practically the same physical actions, all the sounds within the limits of an octave above and an octave below may be reached. In this way we may regard the working capacity of every voice to be theoretically identical, only doubtless being made to differ considerably in scope by individual development.

We are entitled to say that the middle note of the voice is produced by the middle degree or ' mean ' of tension of the vocal cord and air pressure in the breath. The tension or tightness of the cords, and the force of air required to produce vibrations, are regarded as proportionate so long as the vibrating length of cord is not shortened, and therefore, in considering the compass of two octaves, the highest note reaches the maximum of tension and air pressure, while the lower octave reaches the minimum of the same.

It is the law of vibrating strings that the ' tension increases in proportion to the square of the vibrations.' If, then, the vibrations of the lowest note of the compass be taken as 1, the middle note will be 2, and the upper note 4, each one in rising an octave being the double of the other. But the tension increases as the square of the vibrations, so that if the tension of the lowest note is 1, that for the middle note is $2^2=4$, and for the top note of the compass $4^2=16$. As the air pressure follows very much the same proportion as the tension, it will be seen at once that in rising through the scale, the increase of tension and pressure required for every higher note is greater and greater the higher we get, and to add another note to the top of the compass requires no small additional effort.

The actual figures [1] given in the table to represent

---

[1] From Schäfer's *Physiology*.

TABLE OF VOCAL CAPACITY

Air pressure	Tension ratio	Vibrations ratio	Compass	
Extreme (1000 mm.)? water	25	5	high extension	
High . . (640)	16	4	octave	working capacity
	9	3	← centre →	
Medium . (160)	4	2		
Low . . (40)	1	1	low octave	
			extension	

H

the increase of tension and breath pressure are used only to indicate the principle upon which higher notes are produced by the full length of the vocal cords. They cannot be regarded as being scientifically accurate. The vibrations of the vocal cords are not like those of a free string, subject only to longitudinal tension. They concern the elastic edges of two membranes, and the paths of vibration are limited and subject to lateral tension.

Some modification, therefore, must be made in the actual figures, on account of those considerations. This subject is extremely difficult to investigate experimentally. But the fact remains that the proportionate increase of tension and breath pressure increases rapidly the higher we go. This indicates the danger that is encountered in attempting to sing too high.

There is, however, another way in which higher notes can be produced. When the vocal cords are more tightly pressed together the vibrations at their back ends, in the neighbourhood of the vocal processes, are interfered with by compression, or 'stopped.' A higher note is thus produced without increase of tension or air pressure, but the sound is smaller and thinner than that produced by the whole length of the cords. I call these notes 'compressed' as distinguished from the 'free' notes produced by the cords vibrating from end to end.

The determination of the natural compass of the voice is a matter which requires considerable care and a thorough examination of its capabilities both as regards its lowest and its highest notes. If any voice is capable of producing a very low note, it is impossible that it can also produce very high ones without

TABLE OF VOICE TYPES

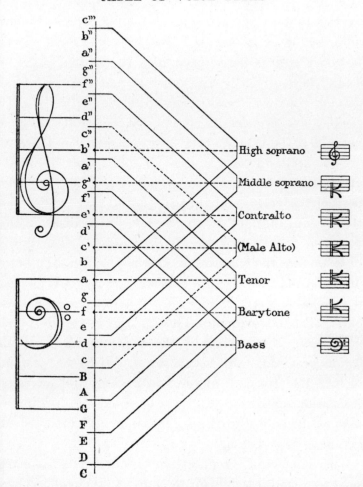

compression. I would therefore recommend careful estimation of the lowest note in every case.

The common variety of man's voice has its central

note on about f. An entirely unpractised voice may not have a compass of as much as two octaves, but an ordinary voice of average capacity finds no difficulty in attaining to that range. Thus we should place the average man's voice with f as its middle, f' as its highest note, and F as its lowest. The true bass voice should be considered as based upon d in the middle, rising to d' and falling to D. The tenor should then be placed upon a, rising to a' and falling to A.

It is not intended to convey the idea that the upper notes, d' of the bass, f' of the barytone, and a' of the tenor are the limits of those voices. It is so much the habit of musicians to write their vocal music for the upper part of the voice, and even above it, that every voice that would attempt to sing has to be trained in this direction to the utmost of its capacity. The power of extending the compass about one-third in an upward direction may be safely conceded, but it would be well if composers would realise that it is for occasional use only. The too frequent use of this upper extension, and, in general, the forcing of the voice upwards, is the commonest cause of vocal ruin. With the practice of increased freedom of the vocal cords, and increased resonation, extension downwards of one-third, or more, may easily be acquired also, but it is seldom called for except in part-singing.

The subject of ' compression ' is one which has many sides to it, and it is difficult to be fair to them all. There can be no doubt, however, about certain points with regard to it.

Compression, like every other mechanical action of

the cords, is not directly voluntary, but merely happens in connection with the striving for high notes. The relief from tension and air pressure is very marked, and ease is at all times desirable in natural processes. In women's voices especially, in which breath control is often weaker, and the power of resonation comparatively stronger than in men's, allowance must be made in its favour. But it is well to bear in mind that the sound of compressed notes is smaller than that of 'free' notes. They are best adapted to piano passages, for when forced they are hard and penetrating. That singers, who are high sopranos by virtue of compression and not by nature, usually lose the middle notes of their voices, can be explained by the bending of the vocal processes and changes in the compressed portions of the cords themselves. A voice which is like two voices, with a rich sound on low notes and a hard shrill sound on high notes, and an uncertain gap in between, is almost certain to be one of these. An exact parallel in a man's voice is not common. The much compressed note is so different from the full free note that it could not often be used except by small tenor voices. There are, however, degrees of compression. When slight it naturally makes less difference, but when considerable its sound would be recognised at once as 'falsetto,' which cannot be regarded as natural to a man's voice.

Among women the three types of voice fall for the ordinary middle variety upon g', with a compass up to g'' and down to g. The contralto, with its centre on e', rises to e'' and falls to e. The true high soprano has its centre upon b', rises to b'' and falls to b. All that I have said with regard to extension upwards and downwards applies to women's voices in the same way as to men's, but there is no doubt that compressed notes are much more commonly used among women than among men, and many women destroy the beauty of their natural voices in the endeavour to make them as high as possible.

It may be said generally that the speaking voice is pitched at and below the centre of the compass, while the singing voice is used mostly above the centre.

There is a certain analogy between the natural types of voice and the musical clefs. (See Table, p. 105.) The bass and tenor clefs are absolutely suited to those voices having the middle note upon the third line. The barytone clef, rarely used, is well suited to the middle type of man's voice for the same reason. The 'soprano clef' is similarly applicable to the middle type of woman's voice. The alto clef, however, is too low for a woman's contralto voice, and is better suited to a male alto. The woman's deep voice is adapted to a clef in which c' is on the second line, which may be called the mezzo-soprano clef. The high soprano, which is a rare form of natural voice, finds its appropriate clef in the treble or 'violin' clef commonly used at present.

It is important to all voices that the middle note of the compass should be recognised, and all vocalising should start upon this note, and be developed smoothly and evenly in both directions until the full compass of two octaves is reached.

Before proceeding to practise the vibrator it is

essential to determine, as accurately as possible, the size of the vocal cords, that is to say, we must know the natural pitch of the voice we are considering. In speaking, when the vocal note is not definitely organised, but merely used to make speech audible and to convey the sense of phrases by natural inflection, it is not necessary to do more than guard the voice from the habit of raising itself to too high a pitch. The general pitch of an ordinary speaking voice may be compared with what corresponds to the lower middle region of the types of voices, which we have already considered. It will then at once be discovered whether a voice has adopted too high a pitch or not.

An easy pitch may be chosen about a third below the centre note. The range of inflection need not be more than a fifth in either direction for all practical purposes.

It is not advisable to direct or prompt the inflections of the voice too much for fear of introducing unnatural ones. When the breath and not the throat is made responsible for the sound of the voice, the natural inflections possess greater intensity and meaning, without covering so large a range of pitch as when the common forms of constriction are allowed to perform their vocal antics unrestrained.

In the case of a voice that is only good for speaking, it may not be possible to go further than indicate a general pitch ; but in the great majority of cases it is possible to find the central note, within a semitone or so, which should be used for practice.

In the case of singing students, this must be ascertained with the greatest care, as the whole future of the voice may depend upon it. If any error should be committed, it is better that it should be below rather than above the true middle.

The first point to notice is the lowest note which can be produced by the vocal cords. The points to be deduced from it are, that if a woman's voice can sing down to ƒ it cannot be a high soprano, and when a man sings down to E he cannot be a high tenor.

In entirely untrained voices it is not wise to take the upper limit of the compass into consideration before definite practice has been undertaken to secure the onset and the continuity of the middle notes, by the proper action of the breath, and without ' shock of the glottis ' or any other similar contraction. It is always quite safe to start a little initial practice upon a note an octave higher than the lowest possible. Thus a woman's voice that can sing down to ƒ is probably rather below the average in pitch, and could be safely given the note ƒ′ to practise on. In the case of a man singing down to E, the note e would be a good practising note for a probable low barytone.

It must, however, be left to the discretion of the teacher how far the performance of the vibrator is to carry the voice in the direction of song. It is good for the speaker to realise the pitch of his own voice, and the practice of recitation on a continuous note near and below the middle of his voice, will develop all that he requires from the vibrator. He should therefore practise the single note exercises which follow (p. 108).

It is in the practice of the vibrator or vocal reed that the musical faculties are first introduced into the process of voice development. It must not be forgotten that this instrument is in itself unconscious, and cannot be directed in technical study in the same way as when voluntary movements have to be educated, as, for instance, those of the hand in the study of the pianoforte or violin. The education of the vocal reed resolves itself into the regulation of the breath, the only force used, and the cultivation of the mental perception and appreciation of sound. From these facts we may deduce the following general rules:—

(1) To take a good breath immediately before making a sound.
(2) At the moment of singing a note to have already decided in the mind what that note is to be.
(3) The whole instrument, the resonator, to be in position at the onset of the note.
(4) To sing absolutely in tune by relying upon distinctness of mental perception and sufficiency of breath.

The vibrator cannot be practised by itself, that is, its association with a vowel-sound cannot be avoided, since the vocal note is obliged to pass through the resonator.

It is not advisable that all vocal exercises should be

associated with one vowel position only, such as *ah*. All the vowel positions have an equal right to be practised in conjunction with the notes, but the five principal sounds,

oo   aw   ah   eh   ee

are selected for convenience.

As we wish to deal with the vibrator by itself as much as possible, we shall assume, in this chapter, that whatever vowel position is selected, it must remain absolutely unchanged during the vocal exercise. Every note of a vocal exercise must satisfy the ear as to the quality of the vowel character, and no movement of the jaw, lips, or tongue must be visible.

A full breath is taken through the nose and allowed to pass out through the nose, without allowing the chest to drop. The mouth is then open to the *ah* position, and breath is taken in through the mouth noiselessly, and passed out again with sufficient force to make the already known resonant pitch of *ah* distinctly audible. When this has been repeated several times without any movement of the mouth, the mind should be directed to the perception of the middle note of the compass (Foundation Ex. No. 1, p. 114.)

Into the breathed vowel this note is then to be introduced in such a way that the sound is that of an aspirated vowel, followed by a note, and passing again into an aspirated vowel. An escape of breath after the note ceases should be heard, in order to make sure that no contraction of any kind occurs in the larynx or elsewhere. Care must be taken that the vowel position remains motionless, and that the chest does not drop. The whispered vowel preceding the note should then be gradually shortened and the note itself carefully and gradually prolonged, so as to remain well within the capacity of the breath. Finally the aspirate may be dropped altogether, and the attack of the note should coincide with the onset of the breath. The even continuity of the note then depends upon the even continuity of the breath, and the ' free release ' after the note must indicate an easy and natural cessation of the breath force.

It is advisable to return to the beginning of this exercise and breathe in and out through the vowel-sound alternately with singing a note upon it, first with an aspirate and then without, in this way accustoming the voice to the attack of a note with an open throat, and to avoid the danger of any ' shock of the glottis ' already referred to.

The position of each vowel or consonant is breathed through before sounding the note, and again after it, without movement of the resonator. In the last group the aspirate becomes the corresponding sounding continuant without any change of position.

At first the middle note of the compass is used only (as in Exercise 1) until the attack is accomplished with that definition which the breath gives it, when the force and the sound are simultaneous. Different vowel positions are to be used in turn ; first the five principal vowels, and then all the other vowels on the Resonator Scale. During the entire performance of the note the breath must be even and continuous, but not escaping

FOUNDATION EXERCISE No. 1.

	High Soprano.	Mid. Soprano.	Con-tralto.	Tenor 8ve lower.	Barytone.	Bass.

Centre Vocal Notes.

Ah
Eh
Ee
Aw
Oo

M
N .
L .

F – V
Th – Th
S – Z

whispered resonance   whispered resonance

breath . . . . } note ——————— { breath . . . .

breath . . } note ————————————— { breath .

onset } note ————————————————————— { release

so as to give a breathy character to the note. A candle flame held in front of the mouth must not flicker during the continuation of the note, but when the sound ceases, sufficient breath escapes after it to cause a considerable flickering, or even to blow the candle out.

It must be carefully noted that during the continu-ance of the note the measurement of the waist, as evidenced by the loosening of the belt or waistband, becomes gradually less, and that there is no sinking of the ribs.

At the end of the note the ribs still remain elevated, and the sudden falling in of the upper abdominal wall, just below the end of the breast bone, can be felt distinctly with the hand when the breath is released.

When all these points have been carefully noticed and practised the pupil may undertake the exercise No. 2, p. 116.

In addition to the single notes, I am giving here only one form of vocal exercise. It is graduated and in four sections. Each may be taken separately at first and afterwards in sequence. This foundation exercise is better suited to the even development of the vocal compass than the singing of ordinary scales, and should be written out in various keys for systematic practice, and for every kind of voice.

Similar exercises of all musical intervals, upwards and downwards from a centre, and variously accompanied, would greatly assist singers in accustoming them to the needs of modern music, and in developing the particular refinement of ear which they must have. I do not intend to carry this matter so far in this volume, and prefer to leave it in the hands of a musician.

Whatever the middle note of tne compass may be, it is first chosen as the tonic or key note of the exercises. They should be written out exactly as they have to be sung, and the pupil is to be encouraged to take in every note with the eye before singing it, as that habit forms the foundation of reading music, which is as essential to the art of singing as the reading of words is to the art of speech.

FOUNDATION EXERCISE No. 2.

Centre Note

M
N
L
V (F)
Th (Th)
Z (S)

M
N
L
(F) V
(Th) Th
(S) Z

	as in
M	(Moon)
N	OO
L	oh (Moan)
(F) V	AW (Morn)
(Th) Th	ŏ (Moss)
(S) Z	AH (Mar)
	ŭ (Much)
	er (Mirth)
	ā (Mat)
	ĕ (Met)
	EH (Mate)
	ĭ (Mill)
	EE (Meal)

The exercises are to be sung separately to the five principal vowel-sounds, and afterwards to any of the remaining vowels in the Resonator Scale, with the same careful attention as bestowed upon *ah* in Exercise 1.

These and similar exercises not only form the beginning of vocal practice, but they represent the basis of the working capacity of the voice and are for daily practice throughout the entire life of a singer.

The habit of carefully reading the exercises applies to beginners only, as more proficient singers will usually sing them by heart. I would, however, warn teachers against playing the scales themselves. One chord to indicate the key should be sufficient, and if pupils are unable to sing a scale correctly without further assist-ance, it becomes a question whether they should be encouraged to sing at all.

When the middle range of the compass has thus become well established, its extension in both directions should be undertaken, not by practising high notes, but by moving the centre note gradually by semitones both upwards and downwards, to the extent of a fourth in both directions, and repeating the same exercises. In this manner the full compass of notes for an octave above and below the centre may be practised in their proper relation to one another. Prolonged high notes are to be carefully avoided until considerable efficiency in vocalising throughout the entire two octaves of the voice has been acquired. Prolonged notes should at first be definitely limited to the central region of the compass.

As a general rule, vocalising exercises are not to be continued for longer than ten minutes at a time on

account of the throat constriction and mouth contor-
tion which readily accompany too much practice upon
simple vowels alone. It is therefore advisable always
to practise these for short periods interspersed with
practice of the continuant consonants, which bring the
vowels forward in the mouth. With this in view it is
good to vocalise

M,　　N,　　L,　　V,　　TH,　　Z.

The only difference between the vocalising of these
consonants and that of the vowels is that the resonator
is held in a partly closed position instead of an open one.

The freedom of the breath and absence of any constriction in the throat is as essential to the proper sounding of these consonants as it is to the vowels themselves.

With the lips closed as in the position for *M*, the
centre note should be attacked, continued, and released
through the nose, exactly as a vowel-sound would be
through the mouth as in Exercise 1. Breathing out
strongly through the nostrils when the lips are closed
indicates the position in which the resonator is to be
held. The sounding of a note on *M* causes considerable
vibration to be felt near the nostrils in front, and not in
the throat or at the back of the nose. The tongue is
forward in the mouth with its tip against the lower
teeth, and the teeth are considerably apart.

I have chosen *M* to begin upon because it is one of
those consonants which is usually freer from faulty
pronunciation than most of the others.

The other continuants should then be practised,
following carefully what has been said with regard to
them in the chapter on consonants.

THE COMBINED INSTRUMENTS

HAVING considered the phonological properties of each of the two instruments of the voice, namely the vibrator and the resonator, we must now examine what takes place when these instruments act together, as is the case in the ordinary uses of the voice.

We know that when by an act of breathing out we form the vocal note, the sound so produced is modified in its quality and character by the hollow spaces of the resonator; thus on any note we can impress the character of the vowels and give them proper sonority. But we know that there is attached to every vowel position a particular phonological condition with its distinctive character and resonant pitch. In speech, where the vocal notes are not organised as they are in singing, they simply move unconsciously, and are controlled only with a view to making language intelligible and distinct. Under such circumstances it is not necessary to consider too closely the phonological agreement between the ever-varying vocal note and the rapidly changing resonant pitches of the different vowels.

But in singing, where the performance of vocal notes is musically organised, the power of maintaining both the quality and the character of a vowel-sound throughout a musical phrase is a matter which should be studied as minutely as possible. The problem before us then is, that since we possess only a single resonator how are we to satisfy a whole compass of two octaves of notes with proper resonation ?

We will consider this more theoretical question before going on with our practical study.

In men the resonator has for its position of *ah* a resonant pitch of, let us say, *c″*. The lowest resonance upon the Resonator Scale is *f′*, for *oo* and the back resonance of *ee*.

It will be noticed that *f′* is also a high note in the average man's compass, therefore his resonator will very rarely be in a position to reinforce the primary note of his vocal cords, but generally one of its harmonics or upper partials.

A man with a large resonator and a high voice is sometimes in a position to obtain this remarkable reinforcement of the few notes at the top of his compass on certain vowel-sounds, and that accounts for the marvellous high notes a few of our greatest singers have been able to produce.

In a woman's voice the case is different. While the vocal compass is practically an octave higher than a man's, the pitch of the resonator is barely a third higher. It therefore happens that the lowest notes of the Resonator Scale are brought almost to the middle of the vocal compass, so that its upper octave often coincides with the primary resonant pitches of the vowel-sounds in the neck.

It thus becomes clear that a woman's voice is

proportionately more deeply resonated than a man's, and is therefore more liable to sudden changes in resonation, owing to the greater distance between the reinforced harmonics of its vocal notes.

We therefore meet with frequent so-called ' breaks,' due to this cause, which destroy the even tone of the instrument, and have to be overcome by very careful adjustment of the resonator.

The manner in which the reinforcement and resonation is carried out is practically as follows.

In every reinforcing or resonating system there is a certain amount of latitude in its function, that is, it will reinforce a particular note and its immediate neighbours a little above and a little below it, the only difference being that in the case of the more perfectly adjusted vibrations the reinforcement is stronger.   Open resonators have a wider range of adaptation than the more enclosed.   A very little power of expansion, and the reverse, of a resonant hollow, goes a long way towards remedying this inequality, and we find that a range of about one-third can be obtained for a resonator under such circumstances.   It is precisely this action that takes place in the voice.

If in the vowel position *ah* with the resonant pitch c'' the deep bass note C should be sung, the reinforcement of the eighth harmonic can be heard, with some practice.

When the vocal note rises a semitone to C sharp the resonant reinforcement in the mouth will be heard to rise to c'' sharp, but on reaching D the resonant reinforcement in the mouth falls again to c'', that being the

HARMONIC REINFORCEMENT.

seventh harmonic ; this in its turn will be heard to rise to d'' when the vocal note reaches E, but when the vocal note touches F the sixth harmonic c'' is heard again. When the bass note rises to G the reinforcement in the mouth may rise to d'', but with the vocal note of A flat the reinforcement will fall to the fifth harmonic on c'', and so on, as shown in the accompanying diagram, always remembering that when the reinforcement in the vowel position is strained upwards it has the alternative of further expanding to catch a harmonic on b', that is, a semitone lower than c''.

In this way, with little or no conscious movement beyond that of a desire to keep expanded, satisfactory reinforcement of all the notes of the compass is to be obtained, each vowel position having its own series of reinforcements based upon its pitch on the Resonator Scale heard in the whispering voice.

So far, however, we have considered only the extreme low notes of a bass voice, for it is especially in these that the reinforcements of the harmonics are most easily distinguished. As the vocal notes rise in the scale, the resonating properties of the vowel positions naturally fall upon lower harmonics, which are also wider apart from one another. Thus the phonological difficulties increase as we rise in the scale. But very soon the reinforcements are more clearly heard an octave higher, that is, among harmonics that are not so far distant from one another. As the accompanying table is, I believe, the first of its kind that has ever been made, and as this field has scarcely yet been subjected to repeated investigation, it is not yet possible to say positively what the law is with regard to these reinforcements. As far as the matter has gone at present I am only in a position to say what the results of my own observations are, and the conclusions which I am inclined to draw from them. The problems of multiple resonation, that is, the resonation taking place in several communicating cavities, has hardly been touched by physicists. The fact also that the human resonator is at least a double one and not a single 'funnel shaped' tube, as it was regarded by the older physiologists, reopens the whole question on a new basis.

In all investigations of sound it is almost impossible to obtain pure vibrations, that is to say, vibrations without harmonics, so that when I speak of the resonant pitches of the vowels, I cannot mean more than that a particular primary resonant note is heard which is more powerful than any of the other subsidiary notes that must of necessity be involved in it.

Thus, when I come to sound the deepest notes of the bass voice and hear very distinct reinforcements of its harmonics by the primary resonant notes, most likely their octaves are also present. Therefore the distinctness of the higher octave, further up in the scale, may be due to its merely coming more prominently into notice when the primary note is in some difficulty of finding vibrations to suit it.

There is, however, another view to take of this. The resonator itself is composed of two chambers, that of the mouth being open at both ends, and that in the neck open at one end only, the vibrating

' reed ' being regarded in physics as a closure of the resonator at the lower end. Thus it is quite likely to be the case that the resonant pitches of the vowels are correctly stated on the Resonator Scale for the cavity in the neck, but that the resonances of the mouth belonging to a tube open at both ends ought really to be regarded as an octave higher. Personally, I am inclined to this view but have not altered the Resonator Scale, because the actual pitch of the notes therein contained is not so important as their relations to one another, and it matters little, for instance, in the lower six members, whether the notes heard are in unison or whether they should be considered octaves.

In estimating high resonances it is often difficult to discriminate between the pitch of a harmonic and its octave, and when they occur together the upper one is generally more distinct than the lower. But the fact that the upper resonances are often heard an octave higher does not affect the practical purposes of the Resonator Scale.

In some further experiments with the reinforcements of the upper members I have recently been able to obtain the complete series of resonances from *ah* (V) to *ee* (XII) upon the notes of the scale from *C* to *c*.

As seen in the table, the resonance of *ah* (V) is upon the eighth harmonic, where the harmonic scale of tones and semitones begins. It is therefore a simple matter for these high resonances to find harmonics in accord with their respective pitches. But on rising through

TABLE OF HIGH HARMONICS ON DEEP BASS NOTES.

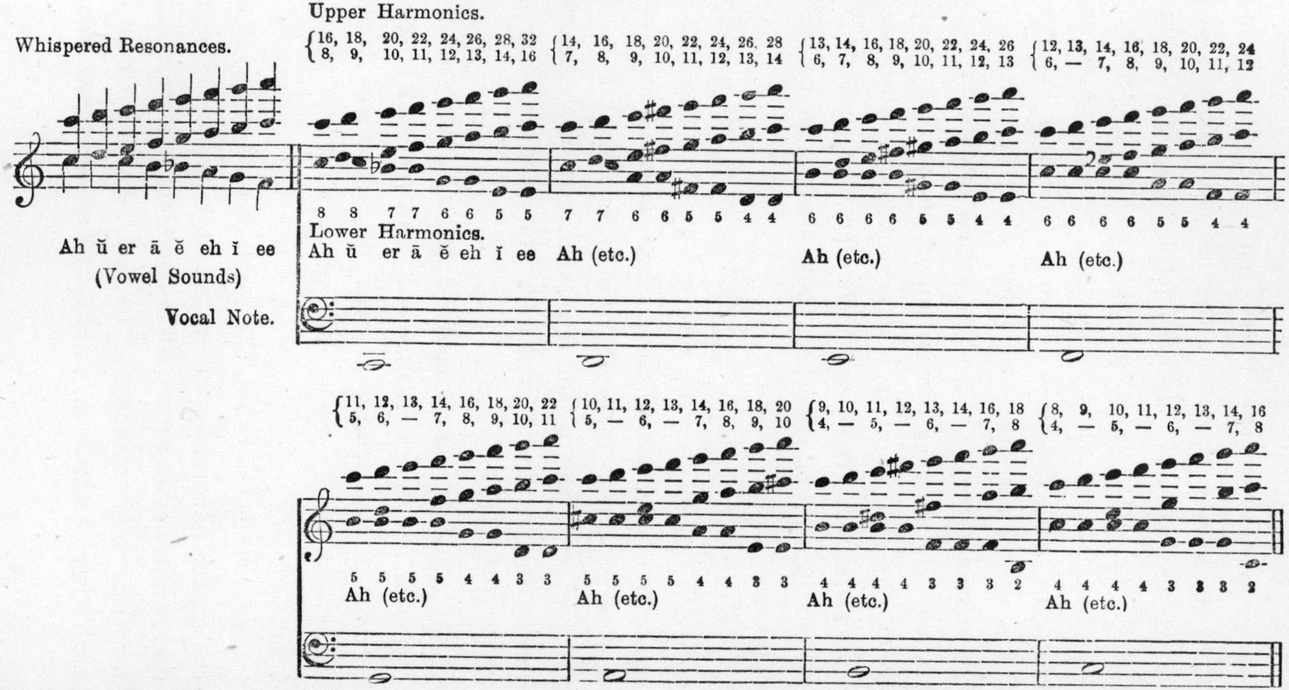

the scale from C to c, the resonant reinforcements an octave higher are audible and remain intact for each note up to B, which shows that they belong to the series beginning on the sixteenth harmonic, and not that which begins upon the eighth of C. The presence of these high harmonics is characteristic of the forward pronunciation of the vowels. The back resonances distinctly belong to the lower octave as given in the Resonator Scale. On rising through the scale from C they adapt themselves to the seventh and lower harmonics. When the vocal note rises above c they often fail to find suitable harmonics, but the expansion in the neck has the effect of making the lower harmonics of the vocal note itself especially prominent, thereby no doubt enriching the general tone of the voice.

It should not be forgotten that the sound produced by the vibrator itself is also composite, that is, it contains numerous harmonics of its own apart from those which are made prominent by the resonator; and a strong third harmonic accompanies the vocal note almost constantly, especially when full resonation in the neck is given to the note. It would thus appear that, when the resonator is large and the throat open, not only the primary note of the vibrator, but also its lower harmonics, can pass out intact. The general richness of a well-resonated voice must depend upon the magnitude of its lower harmonics, and the conditions which favour them are therefore to be studied and cultivated.

All these facts are capable of demonstration to

those who are accustomed to the analysis of sound by the unaided ear, and they go far to prove how it is from the high-pitched resonances in the front of the mouth that the vowel characters are derived, and how the deep resonances in the neck are more concerned with the sonority of the total sound of the voice.

Another important factor in the full richness of the voice is the resonance of the nose.

The nasal cavity and its tributary sinuses take part in the formative process of the nasal consonants, M, N, and $\widehat{NG}$, in all of which the passage through the mouth is entirely obstructed and the sound passes through the nose, but they also take part in the important function of adding to the sonority of the whole voice.

Nasal quality can never be permitted to become prominent in English vowel-sounds, but that does not mean that nasal resonance is entirely absent. On the contrary, it is always present in a well-resonated voice. The question is one of degree only. The wider open the throat, and the more fully resonant the mouth and neck, the more freely may the passage to the nose remain open.

Nasal resonance is therefore an adjunct to the normal full resonance of the two principal cavities of the resonator.

Its presence is regulated by the opening into the nose, controlled by the more or less unconscious soft palate.

We have therefore to rely upon the feeling of vibration in the nose to make us aware of the extent to which it is used. When this sensation is very distinct, the nasal resonance will probably be excessive. When, however, vibration is felt in the breath, and good resonation in the front of the mouth, the nasal quality will generally be unnoticeable, although it may be present in abundance.

The table given (p. 122) of the five principal vowels, impressing their character upon a scale sung, in this instance, by a bass voice, is an illustration of the definite principle upon which all the vowels adjust themselves to the varying notes of the scale. By the same power of adaptation they not only succeed in reaching suitable harmonics for resonation, but can exercise discretion in influencing the general tone of the voice.

When we possess a delicate instrument to record these subtle components of vocal sound, their investigation will be greatly facilitated.

Such phonological problems are extremely complicated, and it is quite unnecessary for the vocal student to enter into their details. Those who teach and are otherwise interested in the subject may find considerable interest in working out these reinforcements for their own and other voices. They must not forget that the open jaw and forward tongue are essential to the value of their experiments.

It is in this way, then, that we explain the fact that every vocal note finds the reinforcement of its harmonics in the hollow spaces of the resonator. The hollow of the neck is mostly concerned in the function of giving sonority to the total sound. The hollow of the mouth, on the other hand, is occupied with those changes of shape which impress upon every sound their particular characteristics.

These two functions of the resonator should not be confused with one another.

According to the Resonator Scale the positions for the vowels are practically fixed according to phonological principles, and designed to secure the full exercise of both functions, and so give both sonority and distinctness to the voice. The question of how much sonority is to be utilised is optional. For instance, in public speaking as well as in singing, a maximum of sonority may be desirable, whereas in ordinary conversation it may not be necessary. Hence the full expansion of the hollow of the neck may be reserved for the best performances of the voice. Under no circumstances, however, can the necessity for distinctness be dispensed with. The clear and open positions of the mouth and the decisive movement of the lips, tip of the tongue and jaw, which constitute what is known as ' forward diction,' are essential to the formation of words under all circumstances.

From this it follows that in singing a series of notes upon a single vowel-sound, the organs of articulation, which are visible from the front, must be immoveable or the vowel character will suffer change. Certain variations in the hollow of the neck certainly do take place, but they become almost an unconscious part of the singer's art of expression. The integrity of the word, which depends largely upon the constancy of its vowel-sound, must not be violated so long as the words are to be dignified by any meaning in the art of song.

It is thus apparent that in using the voice we are practically, as well as theoretically, playing upon two instruments, one the vibrator—which produces the notes in obedience to our mental perception, and acts independently as a musical instrument in singing, or as simply a means of making the voice audible in speech, raising it or lowering it in pitch, prolonging or interrupting it, strengthening or weakening it in force under the mechanical control of the breath.   The other instrument—the resonator—acting on a different principle, performs an entirely independent series of evolutions, transforming the sound of the voice into the manifold characteristics of articulate speech.   It can perform all these, though feebly, in a whispering voice out of a current of breath alone, but when assisted by the vibrating note its influence can be made to carry to a great distance.

The dissociation of the two instruments of the voice must not only be fully recognised, but also carried out carefully in practice.   Much of the control of the vocal note, as I have already indicated, depends upon the management of the breath, and this control is therefore exercised in that neighbourhood where the ' central' breathing is most active, namely, that region near the lower end of the breast bone where the lower ribs expand and the descent of the diaphragm is felt.   On the other hand, the positions of the vowels bring their characteristic sounds as far forward in the mouth as possible.   The movements of the consonants employ the tip of the tongue, the lips and the teeth, so that all that concerns articulate language is referred to the most forward part of the resonator. This separation of the two regions in which the conscious activity of each instrument must be definitely realised, is one of the fundamental principles of the use and development of the voice, and is absolutely in accord with the physical and physiological distinctions between the two instruments.

A few practical exercises will illustrate these principles.

Carefully following the directions given for breathing and whispering, the breath should be made to pass out freely through the five principal vowel positions without any effort or emphasis, so that their resonant notes are definitely heard by the pupil himself.

It is not necessary to make them audible at a distance, as in a stage whisper, but a gentle flow of breath will not only give the resonant note, but also the sense of an open throat, which is essential.

In the first group there is movement of the tongue

only, and in the second of the lips only, but the jaw is stationary in both.

When these have become smooth and easy, the vocal note is introduced with all the precautions laid down in a previous chapter (page 114).

The centre note of the compass is chosen first. Its clearness, steadiness, and continuity are to be un-affected by the vowel changes.

In order to make sure of the vowel positions, and of the change from one to another, breathe through them quietly, alternately with the vocal exercise, and note that the breathing is even and continuous in both cases, as it would be with a single vowel—the only change is in the position of the tongue and lips, which must not affect the steadiness of the breathing or note in any way.

The whole group of six continuant consonants are practised in a similar manner on the same note.

This exercise is found difficult at first, but it should be persevered with, so as to acquire complete control of the lips and the tip of the tongue during the even continuity of breath and vocal note.

The six continuant consonants are then brought into contact with the five principal vowels by sounding them in pairs, care being taken to make them both free and continuous.

When the single notes have been accomplished, the moving notes may be undertaken as in the exercises suggested for the vibrator.

Each of the sections of the Foundation Exercise should be taken in turn, and all the syllables com-pounded of the continuant consonants and five principal

FOUNDATION EXERCISE No. 3.

Central Note.

Ah	Eh	Ee	Eh	Ah	Aw	Oo	Aw	Ah

| M | N | | L | V | T͡h | | Z |

Mah	Meh	Mee	Meh	Mah	Maw	Moo	Maw	Mah
Nah	Neh	Nee	Neh	Nah	Naw	Noo	Naw	Nah
Lah	Leh	Lee	Leh	Lah	Law	Loo	Law	Lah
Vah	Veh	Vee	Veh	Vah	Vaw	Voo	Vaw	Vah
T͡hah	T͡heh	T͡hee	T͡heh	T͡hah	T͡haw	T͡hoo	T͡haw	T͡hah
Zah	Zeh	Zee	Zeh	Zah	Zaw	Zoo	Zaw	Zah

Fah	Feh	Fee	Feh	Fah	Faw	Foo	Faw	Fah
T͡hah	T͡heh	T͡hee	T͡heh	T͡hah	T͡haw	T͡hoo	T͡haw	T͡hah
Sah	Seh	See	Seh	Sah	Saw	Soo	Saw	Sah

Pah	Peh	Pee	Peh	Pah	Paw	Poo	Paw	Pah
Tah	Teh	Tee	Teh	Tah	Taw	Too	Taw	Tah
Kah	Keh	Kee	Keh	Kah	Kaw	Koo	Kaw	Kah
Bah	Beh	Bee	Beh	Bah	Baw	Boo	Baw	Bah
Dah	Deh	Dee	Deh	Dah	Daw	Doo	Daw	Dah
Gah	Geh	Gee	Geh	Gah	Gaw	Goo	Gaw	Gah

In the first set the sound is absolutely continuous.

In the second set the sound is interrupted by the consonants, but the breath force remains continuous, giving to aspirates and explosives their proper character.

vowels applied to them, so that one syllable occupies first a whole bar, then two to the bar, and then one to each note.

The principal points which require careful watching are—

(1) That the breath and the vocal exercise should be smooth and continuous.

(2) That the vowel-sound should always preserve its true character, identical with that of the prolonged vowel however rapidly it may be repeated, and occupy its full share of the value of its note.

When continuity has been thus established, those consonants are to be used which necessarily interrupt the sound—

(aspirates)	F	Th	S
(explosives)	P	T	K
(sounding explosives)	B	D	G

Care should be taken not to practise these too loud or too quickly.

Further advance may then be made to the remaining vowel-sounds of the Resonator Scale. Groups, such as those given for the practice of the resonator (page 94), after having been carefully whispered, are applied to the exercises in the same way as the principal vowels, first with the continuant consonants and afterwards with the interrupting consonants, always securing good positions by whispering and paying close attention to the resonances, before bringing the vocal notes into them.

PRONUNCIATION CHART[1]

A CHART based upon the Resonator Scale is found useful in teaching and practising pronunciation. The simple and compound vowel-sounds are placed in line at the top of the chart with their resonant pitches above them. In the left-hand column are placed the consonants, both simple and multiple, which are prefixed to the vowel-sounds.

Examples of short words are given and arranged according to the sounds of the vowels that they contain, and the consonants that are prefixed to them.

We thus obtain vertical columns of words with the same vowel-sound following different consonants, and horizontal lines of particular consonants followed by various vowel-sounds. When the consonant is the difficulty it is practised horizontally, and when the vowel is at fault the vertical columns are followed.

The chart here constructed is for the English language, but the application of the Resonator Scale to any language may be carried out in the same way, for the principle of the Resonator Scale is that upon which all languages are formed by the action of the resonator, and only slight modifications are necessary to express

[1] See end of volume.

the subtle differences between what may be considered the same sounds in different languages.

Under all circumstances in the practice of diction it is best to breathe through the words softly and smoothly, so as to make certain of the vowel resonances and good movements for the consonants before using the vocal sound.

In practising the Pronunciation Chart all the words in the vertical columns, when so whispered, should have the same vowel resonance, whereas when whispered along the horizontal lines the whole Resonator Scale should be made distinct. When the vocal sound is introduced care should be taken that the positions of the vowels should be exactly the same as those which have been acquired by whispering.

English. Verse by Tennyson.
Resonator.

VIII-VII	XI	I-XII	XI-I	XI	XI-VII	VIII	III VII	III
There	is	sweet	mu - sic	here	that	softer	falls

VIII	IX VI	IV	II	II IX	IV	VI	V
Than	petals	from	blown	roses	on	the grass,

III	VI-XI	XI-I	IV	XI	III VII	IX XII	III
Or	night - dews	on	still	waters	between	walls

IV	VIII II XI	VIII XI	XI	VI	XII XI	V
Of	shadowy	granite,	in	a	gleaming	pass ;

XI-I XI	VIII	IX XI VII	IV	VI	XI XI	VI-XI
Mu - sic	that	gent - li - er	on	the	spirit	lies,

VIII	VI-XI-VII	VI-XI XI	VI IV	VI-XI-VII	VI-XI
Than	tir'd	eye - lids	upon	tir'd	eyes ;

XI-I XI	VIII	XI	I-XII	XII	V-I	IV	VI	XI I	VI-XI
Mu - sic	that	brings	sweet	sleep	down	from	the	blissful	skies

XI-VII	V	I	IV IX	XII			
Here	are	cool	mosses	deep.			

VIII	I	VI	IV	XII	VI-XI XI XII		
And	through	the	moss	the	i - vies creep		

VIII	XI	VI	XII	VI	IV XII	V-I-VII	I-XII
And	in	the	stream	the	long-leaved	flowers	weep,

VIII	IV	VI	VIII XI IX	VI	IV XI	VIII	XI	XII
And	from	the	craggy ledge	the	poppy	hangs	in	sleep.

Some lines are given here as an example of how to apply the Resonator Scale to the study of ordinary declamation. Over every word the proper positions of the vowels are indicated by the Roman numbers of the Resonator Scale. By slowly breathing out these words the proper resonant positions of the vowels and movements of the consonants can be determined before any vocal sound is used.

The power of using the speech organs slowly and steadily upon an out-breath, as indicated here, gives, with practice, that control which is the key to good diction.

VOCAL CAPACITY AND SONG DIAGRAMS

It is not the intention of phonological science to carry the vocal exercises any further into the art of music than the simple technique of continuous notes, sequences and intervals would warrant. Thus far we are entitled to regard the formative process of voice cultivation as a scientific subject based upon natural law. It remains, therefore, for the musician to take up the completion of vocal performance in the art of song at this point. He may then bring all that art can suggest into the service of the voice as his instrument of expression, remembering always that there are special principles attached to the human organs, in the same way as they are attached to the violin and other instruments that he uses, which should not be contravened. A musical composer who understood the nature of the voice would have satisfaction in feeling that the performance of his music was at the same time improving and perfecting the human voice as an instrument of musical expression.

There can be no doubt that the tone of a violin improves by being played upon when in the hands of a great master, but that, on the other hand, some kind of playing might in itself be detrimental to the instrument. It is also well known that considerably altering the pitch, for instance, of a beautiful violin, may have anything but a good effect upon it. How much more, then, is it not the case in the sensitive, elastic, living instrument of the voice, depending for its existence upon the manner in which it has been developed and the manner in which it continues to be used, that it would be ruined if condemned to uses beyond its natural capacity.

Composers delight in high notes, and in all kinds of effects, many of which may be beautiful, while others only startle and arrest attention. But they should not forget that while they are possibly advancing their reputation in the ears of the public, they may, at the same time, be crushing the life and livelihood out of that very instrument which they ought to worship as the most human of all means of musical expression.

. I have had the satisfaction of seeing a celebrated violinist walk off the concert platform, because the pianoforte which was to accompany him was tuned to the high English pitch. He would not run the risk of straining his magnificent Stradivarius.

If singers would take the same care of their voices, composers would probably become more careful in their writing, and conductors might do more to subdue their vocal accompaniments and keep down the general instrumental pitch.

It is not generally known to what extent singers still suffer, even under the so-called ' diapason normal ' $(a' = 435 \cdot 5)$. Mr. Alexander J. Ellis[1] has shown in his

---

[1] *Vide* Helmholtz, *Sensations of Tone*, Eng. Trans. and Appendix by A. J. Ellis.

' History of Musical Pitch' how the general pitch of $a' = 420$, or thereabouts, was prevalent in Europe for two centuries, i.e. all through the great vocal period, up to the beginning of the nineteenth century. The rise to $a' = 452 \cdot 5$ and higher, and the subsequent compromise which reduced it to $a' = 435 \cdot 5$, only gave the singers one-half their due. The instrumentalists forgot that the voice is not physically able to make concessions and compromises, and whatever brilliant quality other instruments may obtain by the higher pitch, the natural limits of the voice, which had determined the general pitch for the two centuries before the growth of the modern orchestra, could not possibly be altered.

The compromise still condemns the singer to sing all the music of classical composers, up to and including Beethoven and Schubert, nearly half a tone higher than the composers intended, even when so-called ' continental' pitch is adopted.

Considering the tendency to write for the upper part of the voice, the additional rise in pitch increases the strain upon the vocal organs very considerably. Modern musicians seldom remember that in studying the vocal music of Mozart, for example, they should mentally transpose it nearly half a tone.

It would be easy to imagine the progress of a modern musical Juggernaut driving in his triumphal car amid the plaudits of the populace along the way strewn with the débris of vocal instruments, shattered in his fierce conflicts with the laws of nature. But this is a scientific treatise in which the imagination is not to be indulged. Fortunately we have a more accurate method of procedure. By constructing what is called the 'Song Diagram' we can estimate, as accurately as we wish, the actual work demanded by any vocal composition. By comparison of such a diagram with the normal capacity of the voice, it becomes apparent to what voice the composition is suitable and what are its particular demands in vocal performance, and so we come at once to dispassionate conclusions.

In constructing the 'Song Diagram' it is not necessary to be punctilious about semitones, so that for the sake of simplicity, and in order to lighten a somewhat laborious task, we neglect accidentals and regard the scale as represented by lines and spaces without signatures. Upon special paper ruled in squares a vertical line is drawn representing the scale, and into the squares are placed dots, one for the value of every quaver or whatever unit we select. The usual plan is to regard the square as filled when eight dots have been put into it. In going through the voice parts of the work we obtain an estimate of all the notes, expressed in quaver units as dots, and measured in squares in a horizontal direction as regards duration, and upon the scale in a vertical direction as regards pitch. When the work is finished the squares are darkened, the full ones entirely, and those that are not entirely filled, at the ends of the lines, are darkened in proportion to the number of dots in them.

The diagram then shows us not only the range of voice covered by the composition, but also where most of the work lies.

Thus estimated, we find that the work required by

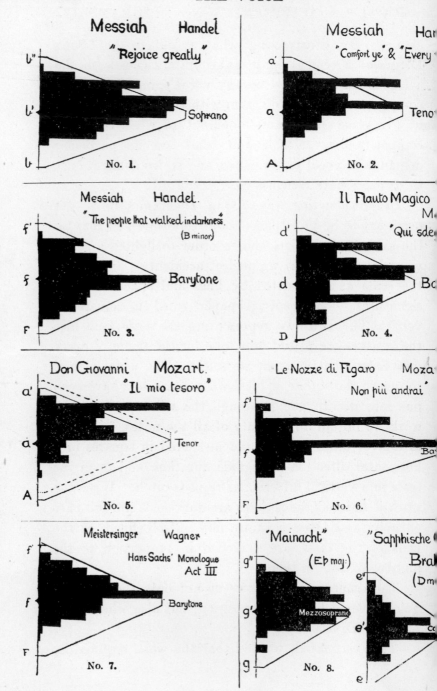

Messiah   Handel
"Rejoice greatly"
Soprano   No. 1.

Messiah   Han
"Comfort ye" & "Every
Teno   No. 2.

Messiah   Handel.
"The people that walked in darkness".
(B minor)
Barytone   No. 3.

Il Flauto Magico
M
"Qui sde
Ba   No. 4.

Don Giovanni   Mozart.
"Il mio tesoro"
Tenor   No. 5.

Le Nozze di Figaro   Moza
"Non più andrai"
Ba   No. 6.

Meistersinger   Wagner
Hans Sachs' Monologue
Act III
Barytone   No. 7.

"Mainacht"
(Eb maj.)
Mezzosoprano   No. 8.

"Sapphische
Bra
(Dm

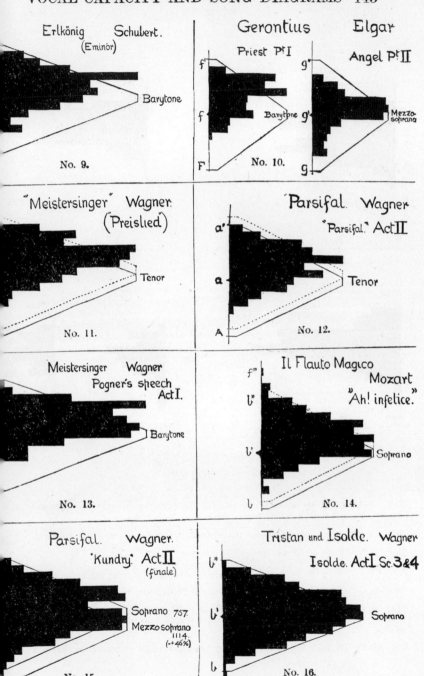

Erlkönig   Schubert.
(E minor)

Barytone

No. 9.

Gerontius   Elgar
Priest Pt I   Angel Pt II

f'   g"

f   g'
    Barytone   Mezzo-soprano

F   g
No. 10.

"Meistersinger" Wagner.
("Preislied")

Tenor

No. 11.

Parsifal. Wagner.
"Parsifal." Act II

a'

a
    Tenor

A   No. 12.

Meistersinger   Wagner
Pogner's speech
            Act I.

Barytone

No. 13.

Il Flauto Magico
            Mozart
        "Ah! infelice."

f'''
b"

b'
    Soprano

b   No. 14.

Parsifal.   Wagner.
"Kundry." Act II
        (finale)

Soprano 757.
Mezzo soprano
    1114.
(-+46%)

No. 15.

Tristan und Isolde. Wagner
    Isolde. Act I Sc. 3 & 4

b"

b'
    Soprano

b   No. 16.

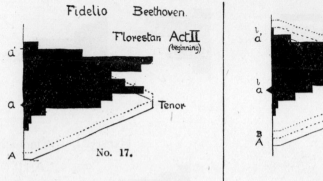

No. 17.

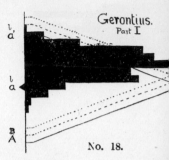

No. 18.

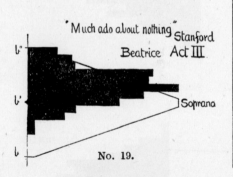

No. 19.

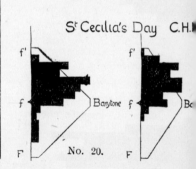

No. 20.

NOTES

Nos. 1-8.   Good examples of writing for the voice indicated. The prolongation notes is not extreme.

Nos. 9, 10.   Not so good—except the second part of No. 10, which is excellent.

Nos. 11, 12.   Both strain the Tenor voice to the full.

No. 13.   High for Barytone. The part is said to be for a Bass.

No. 14.   Good—but for a phenomenally high Soprano with a high note 'in alt.'

Nos. 15, 16.   Very full work for true Soprano voice. Should not be attempted by a soprano, which voice would have to bear an estimated additional st $46\,°/_0$ in No. 15.

Nos. 17, 18, 19, 20.   All too high or 'top-heavy,' though without going beyond the h any given composition is shown diagrammatically in somewhat triangular form, which can be compared with the similar form in which we have already expressed the normal vocal capacity. What we learn from this comparison is that a composition is best suited to that voice in which the bulk of the work falls near the centre of the vocal compass. The centre of the voice and its immediate neighbourhood must always be regarded as best fitted for continuous work; it is therefore quite as important to apply to it the bulk of work required, as to keep the limits of the compass of the composition within the limits of the compass of the voice (pp. 103, 105).

It is a common practice amongst musicians to regard only these limits, and to say of any musical composition that it is suited to a particular voice because it does not go higher or lower than the compass of that voice, but this assumption is frequently erroneous. There are many compositions written for the voice within the limits of the treble clef, which, although they could be reached by the lower female voices, are in reality only suitable to the high soprano. The musical practice of writing for the upper string of the violin or violoncello for the sake of effectiveness, may not damage those instruments, but if the same principle is carried out in writing for the voice, very serious mischief may result. It is quite legitimate for composers to write for rare voices only, if they like, but if they think that by restricting their works to the treble clef, for instance, they are suiting the generality, they are profoundly mistaken.

When a voice performs any work in which its

maximum use lies well in the middle of its capacity, it gives to the singer that sense of ease and suitability so necessary to proper expressiveness, and whatever high notes may occur at the uppermost limit of the compass, they are certain to possess a better quality than those from a voice that has been constantly strained.

The triangular figure expressing the ' Vocal Capacity ' of the various types of voices is drawn over the ' Song Diagram ' to show whether the maximum work corresponds with the maximum power of doing work. It is not intended to be laboriously exact, because to be of general use a considerable amount of latitude must be permitted ; but if the bulk of the work lies much above the centre of the voice, in spite of not exceeding the limits, at least the fatigue of its performance will be explained.

It becomes clear, therefore, that the composer is not definitely able to state for what voice he has written his music until he has estimated the work that it requires by means of a ' Song Diagram.' If the ' Song Diagram ' were printed upon the cover of the book, the singer would know beforehand whether the study of the work would be a strain to his voice or not. Every singer should know exactly where the centre of his voice lies, because that should have been the foundation of all his vocal practice from the first. If he cares sufficiently for the instrument upon which his art, and possibly also his livelihood depends, he will take care to protect himself against strain by avoiding works which obviously lie too high, although they may not go outside his compass.

Singers often complain that they are obliged to sing what composers have written for their voices, which is perfectly true, from a worldly point of view. That difficulty may, however, now be remedied, since it is possible for a composer to learn the natural capacity of human voices, as well as the amount of work required by his compositions, by this sufficiently accurate method of observation. There is no longer an excuse for music said to be for the bass voice but which is only suited to barytone, nor for barytone music written entirely upon the upper leger lines of the bass clef, nor for the placing of music for the average female voice well up in the treble clef. The fault of writing too low for the voice is very rarely indulged in. It is, however, a fact that singers sometimes find music too low for them, because their voices have been trained too much in the upward, and not sufficiently in the downward direction.

While discussing this subject I may here refer to the difference that exists between the true vocal compass and the declamatory compass. It has already been explained that the increase of tension and pressure exerted upon the vocal cords in rising to high notes is best sustained in continuous phrases, that is, in lyrical passages and in prolonged notes. The constant cessation and recommencement of sound caused by unvoiced consonants, such as the aspirates and explosives, render the upper fourth of the vocal compass unsuitable for ordinary declamation. This part of the compass is very seldom used in speech except on occasions of great excitement and emotion, and then only in solitary emphatic exclamations. A composer who raises a declamatory passage above the fifth from the centre of the voice he is using, must therefore have very serious reasons for so doing.

Another point to be remembered is that the lowest notes of the vocal compass are naturally of a soft character and cannot be sung ' forte '; but that they furnish some of the most beautiful ' piano ' sounds of the human voice does not seem to be generally appreciated by vocal composers.

The space within these pages only permits of a small number of examples being given. A complete study of this subject would run into many volumes.

GENERAL REMARKS

VOICE LITERATURE

FROM the foregoing scientific and technical details it is evident that the full capacity and good control of the breath, and a well-adjusted and freely moving resonator, are acquisitions from which very few people need consider themselves debarred. Musical perception sufficient to warrant the use of these instruments to some extent in singing, is not so rare a gift, in my own experience, as proficiency in speech. On the contrary, it is quite natural for everyone to be able to sing a little. The question is rather, how far that gift can be carried in the direction of expressing a highly cultivated art like that of music.

For the voice to rank as a real instrument of song it must be able to do more than produce sounds. That 'more' is wholly within the province of the musician, and must therefore be left to the artist for its proper cultivation. But as regards the sounds themselves, the science of phonology claims the sole authority. The problems involved are physical and physiological only. It is only in so far as they are understood in phonology that anything definite can be said about them at all. That musicians should write books attempting to

L

explain the action of the vocal organs according to suggestions by other musicians and supplemented by ideas of their own, cannot do more than acquaint us with the opinions of those authors and show us how much or how little of real physiological fact they have been able to incorporate in their teaching. Such works have their own undoubted importance, but do not furnish us with what we recognise as the truth in science. The truth of vocal principles can only be arrived at through physical and physiological research by those whose knowledge enables them to understand and demonstrate the phenomena they are investigating.

I do not wish to go so far as to advise musicians not to write books about the voice. They are at liberty to say all they know of its final performances. But it is only fair to let them know that deductions from a superficial knowledge of science much more often mislead than enlighten, and that while their consideration of anatomy, etc., may impress the uninitiated, their pseudo-scientific conclusions have the reverse effect upon those who are qualified to criticise them. It is no exaggeration to say that the majority of works on the voice by musicians throw more light upon the author than upon the subject. And yet, if they would only relate as clearly as possible their positive experiences and observations, without omitting any detail, musicians might indicate to phonological science a great many new points for thorough investigation.

For instance, in these pages I have suggested that since the sound of the voice depends upon breath pressure, the best way to maintain and regulate it is by preserving the costal expansion until the diaphragm is replaced. Some practical teachers may have other methods of breathing. If they have, they should describe them accurately and cause definite experiments to be made with a ' spiro-dynameter ' to show whether they are more efficacious in maintaining and regulating breath pressure than the one here suggested.

The positions of the vowels and movements of the consonants, and the variations they cause in the functions of the resonator, afford endless opportunities for individual research, which the sensitive ears of teachers could materially assist.

The analysis of vocal sound into its components is work that only carefully trained ears, such as theirs, can undertake, and much light might be thrown upon the action of the resonator in producing ' tone ' by such observations.

The vocal cords themselves I should advise musicians to leave alone, for the direct investigation of such an unconscious mechanism is practically beyond their reach.

The indirect examination of the attack, continuity and release of the note, the estimation of the vocal compass and such questions are, however, always before them. Phrasing and expression and all that belongs to the art of music is their own particular province of study, and it is notable in musical literature how little has been written on the subject of Song in comparison with other subjects. So that there is a great deal for them to write about in preference to conjectural physiology.

VOCAL EDUCATION

Once, when stating the general claims of phonology, I was told by a high musical authority that there was so much else which singers had to be taught that their curriculum could not be increased, and I have often wondered since, what so many young singers, turned out year after year, could have devoted their time to in preference to the rudiments of breathing and pronunciation. However much that may be the case, it is also true that a great deal of a singer's training has nothing whatever to do with music.

One of the results of phonological advance is the clear conviction that it has become necessary to re-organise our present system of voice education.

Not even for the sake of argument do I intend to criticise the old system, for it is a far stronger and more truly scientific principle to uphold and promote what is sound, and to leave what is unsound to natural processes. I shall, therefore, simply state the course of voice development which phonological principles would prescribe.

It should be borne in mind that—

(1) Phonological development includes all that concerns the voice from the beginning to the end.
(2) The sounding properties of the voice organs, subject to their own welfare, and to the particular functions they have to perform, are to form the guiding principle of their education.

(3) The road to perfection in song is the same as that which leads to perfection in speech, but goes further.

Children.—Particular care must be taken to provide the new-born infant with ample room in its swaddling-clothes for full expansion of the lungs. Bandages and tapes round the lower ribs are to be discouraged. Every opportunity is to be taken to secure the passage of breath through the nose from the first. No child should be allowed to acquire the habit of breathing through the mouth either night or day. I respect the enlightenment of those American Indian tribes who tie up the babies' mouths when they are not being fed. The infant, thus muted and muzzled, learns to keep quiet and not to bite everything, as well as to breathe through the nose—all inestimable advantages.

Nothing does the nose so much good as breathing through it. I need not go into all the important medical reasons for this. I will only mention that the growth of the upper jaw depends upon the proper dilation of the nasal cavity, and the constantly open mouth produces the undersized lower jaw and receding chin. So that neglect of the nose may be the cause of grave difficulties in the speech organs as well as of adenoids and other obstructions. I should like also to draw attention to the importance of keeping the nose straight. Children should be carefully handled in this respect and taught to use their handkerchiefs with two hands, for the use of one hand only is liable to bend the cartilages.

The sooner children can be taught to stand up

straight and expand their lungs the better. Quite little ones can be induced to heave a few deep sighs through the nose and to use their lower ribs when their chests are gently grasped with both hands. Any nurse can see to this morning and evening with advantage.

When children begin to make sounds it is quite as easy for them to imitate good ones as bad ones, and it is therefore advisable to begin early with the best models. 'Mah-mah' and 'Nah-nah' are to be encouraged with open mouth and nasal consonants. If, however, they should say 'Bah-bah' and 'Dah-dah' some nasal obstruction may be suspected.

Every word a child is taught to say should be considered more from the point of view of its sound than its sense, and carefully pronounced for it to imitate. With the learning of its own native language the child's education begins.

We now come to an important step in our phonological programme.

A teacher who is to guide the process of learning a language ought to be acquainted with the phonological laws of pronunciation. He, or she, ought to be able to watch the organs of articulation, to see that they are properly used, and to help even small children to speak distinctly, if not correctly.

The most enlightened modern Elementary School teachers have, I believe, already gone far in establishing a system by which children become familiar with the sounds of words and the names of objects, before they are troubled with the letters of the alphabet. This interesting process is one in which phonology can be made directly useful, and it is hoped that in the Training Colleges for Elementary Teachers a definite uniform plan in accordance with its principles may finally be adopted.

In the later schools where English Language and Literature, and the Classics and Modern Languages are studied, the principles of pronunciation and vocal sound can be applied directly with less difficulty. It is at that age that children begin to have a little control over their speech organs and can understand the formation of vowels with the mouth open, the free movements of the consonants, the open throat and all such matters that lay in their voices the foundation of future excellence.

The teachers, in both public and private institutions of this kind, already realise the benefit of systematising the subject of pronunciation so that their work may be uniform and continuous in the various departments, and are also aware of the credit they can gain by the good manner of speaking and pronouncing to be heard among their pupils.

Adults.—An important point in connection with the Training Colleges is that the teachers very willingly take up the subject, on account of the benefit to themselves, of learning to manage their own voices to greater advantage. It is in reality a practical necessity to most teachers who have to use their voices for many hours a day. Here, however, we begin to speak of adult teaching.

With the growth of the understanding comes the desire to use the voice in many ways beyond the ordinary limits of conversation. Public speaking of any kind requires some extra training in order to bring the natural uses of the voice up to the level of the demands made upon it. Thus with the full growth of the body the fuller development of the breath and resonating organs is advanced as a necessary part of a man's or woman's equipment for the speaking professions. If good phonological principles have been carried out from the first, very little extra study should be necessary. If, on the other hand, the voice has been entirely neglected up to this point, as is generally the case at present, it is still possible to enter upon the process of acquiring better habits of speech and pronunciation ; but it should be remembered that the later the start, the more difficult the change and the slower the improvement.

Taking all things into consideration, the provision of school teachers with a uniform phonological system is the most promising scheme for improving the national habits of speech. Affecting directly, as it then would, the elementary and secondary, public and private schools, it would naturally find its way into the universities, and very little, if any, additional training would be required for the Church, the Bar, Politics, or the Stage.

Then comes the important vocal question of singing.

Very great care would be exercised in the junior schools, by any masters acquainted with phonology, in the matter of allowing singing. The vocal cords are easily strained during their growth. In girls the growth goes on more or less steadily up to the age of about sixteen or seventeen, so that what was within their compass one year, might be too high for it the next. Boys go through the soprano stage and change rapidly at the end of it, when all singing must cease for about two years or so. Most boys who have beautiful soprano voices strain them during that and the transition period, so that they cannot sing later in life.

A little singing may, of course, be allowed and encouraged in the schools, especially when it is required to be associated with good pronunciation, as it would be in proper hands. But it has to be watched very carefully to guard against strain and fatigue, the ill effects of which may be permanent.

At the age of seventeen, boys and girls may expect to begin their training in singing if their musical faculties are considered worthy of the attempt.

If the right phonological principles have already been applied to the perfection of the speech organs, progress in vocalising can be rapidly made, and such training would not be the arduous struggle which it often is. If the voice has not had that advantage, two years should be spent upon it before attempting to approach the more musical part of the training. To introduce musical phrases into an undeveloped resonator is like playing upon an instrument before it is properly finished, and it is only too likely to end in the disappointments which are so common under the present system from the same cause.

It is therefore necessary that a real voice master should be acquainted with all that phonological science can teach him, for that alone can give him proper authority to deal with the development of the vocal instruments. If he is not a musician he can direct the process as far as the completion of the powers of speech. Only when he adds music to his other qualifications can he be permitted to carry on the instruction into the art of song. But a musician without special phonological knowledge can only be entrusted with the care of a voice which has already been brought to the singing stage by proper training, and it will still be necessary to keep that voice under phonological supervision in order to guard it against habits detrimental to it as a whole, which are not infrequently acquired in the course of musical study. This plan has much to recommend it, for it opens the subject of singing to all qualified musicians, and enables the phonological voice master to watch the whole process and correct in good time errors which are too often allowed to continue until they have done permanent harm.

From this account of phonological voice education it might be thought that the province of the singing master is being invaded. But that is not exactly the case. Phonology insists only upon the great difference between a singing master and a voice master. There is no reason why a master should not be both, by being doubly qualified in music and phonology, but with a single qualification only, he cannot be more than one or the other. As a musician he has a large field open to him in bringing the enormous amount of music which is written for the voice to the perfection of its interpretation. That is his real province, and he is not entitled to go outside it unless he is prepared to undertake the whole development of the instrument he employs. If he does so he is bound to qualify himself in the knowledge that enables him to recognise and to direct the education of all the elements that combine to form the singing voice. What science can teach him of that purely physiological process he, as a voice master, must then know. And when the problems of breathing and the training of the speech organs are brought before him, he must be able to undertake their complete cultivation without any uncertainty or vagueness. He must be able to teach the full phonological value and linguistic accuracy of the sounds of language, since every vocal note emitted must pass through the resonator.

Indeed, as already indicated, the work of the voice master has most to do with breathing and the production of speech by the resonator. The vibrating vocal cords are so unconscious that teaching, except as regards the onset, continuity and cessation of their sound, can hardly be said to apply to them. It is, therefore, by the excellence of the breath control and speech organs that a voice master would expect to be judged, and fine phrasing and diction are the best evidence of good training. Vocalising betrays more often the competence or incompetence of the singer than of the master, although its technique may be facilitated by the proper control of the other factors.

The course of phonological instruction which is here advocated for teachers of all subjects which involve speaking or singing is the same, and includes—

(1) Study of respiration and the best means of acquiring a full volume of air and complete control over it.

(2) Study of the resonator and all its functions in producing the sounds of language and the tone of vocal sound.

(3) Study of the vibrator and the natural principles of producing vocal notes.

(4) Study of general vocal requirements in all branches of speaking and singing.

A special institution for the pursuit of these studies does not at present exist, nor is it as yet decided whether existing allied institutions will open departments for that purpose. The subject itself is not a new one, but the phonological way of regarding it is not yet fully understood by educational authorities. The general interest in it, however, increases, and the volume of our phonological knowledge is being extended by research, and those who are working at it are better satisfied with gradual changes than with excited or over-advertised reforms.

VOICE PRESERVATION

It is not possible to leave the subject of voice education without adding something on behalf of its proper preservation.

The vibrator upon which the sound depends is extraordinarily tenacious and active, but in the greater performances of the voice it is subjected to very considerable strain. The wonder is that so powerful a sound can be produced by so small an organ. It has, however, its limitations like every other living organ, and like these also, when habitually overtaxed, is liable to changes which destroy its natural function beyond recovery. In the tender years of growth this is most particularly the case, and a whole lifetime of beautiful sound can easily be sacrificed for the sake of a little showing off in childhood. It is only with the completion of manhood and womanhood that the flower of the voice attains its true significance. There is no gainsaying this great vital fact, and the ancient maxim that ' children should be seen and not heard ' is as true in ordinary life as it is upon the stage and public platforms.

In adult life, especially when the voice is important to a profession, as much care should be bestowed upon the sounding instrument as would be given to any of the other organs of special sense. Those who value their eyes should not habitually read until the sight fails, nor is the neighbourhood of cannon or machinery good for the delicacy of the ear, and so also should those who have any caring for the voice avoid shouting or screaming themselves hoarse, whatever their excitement may be.

There are, of course, all the general hygienic precautions, such as the moderation of tobacco and spirits, and the avoidance of dusty and ill-ventilated atmospheres; but what concerns the subject of phonology most particularly is that the whole course of voice training should lead up to the best means of preserving the health of the vocal cords. The development and control of the breath force and its entire responsibility for vocal sound, without any 'glottic shocks' or constrictions in the larynx, give to the vocal cords the proper freedom within the limits of natural compass. The full expansion in the neck by the sterno-thyroid muscles acting from below the larynx, and the free and forward position of the tongue, not only relieve the vocal vibration from any obstruction in the throat, but also, by giving them resonant reinforcement, add to the sound and diminish the strain upon the cords. In fact, the full development of breath control and resonator acts beneficially upon the vibrator and gives it less work to do. Moreover, the mechanisms of the breath and resonator are practically indestructible, and go on steadily improving so long as they are kept up to the mark by gentle exercise. Such exercise, as we know, can be carefully carried out without any sound beyond that of a soft whisper.

In later life the general elasticity of all the tissues to some extent declines, but when the other factors are strongly developed it is often extraordinary to notice how little the vigour of the voice is affected by slight impairment of the cords. Examples of this phenomenon are so numerous that it is unnecessary to mention them.

The life history of the voice points so emphatically to the resonator as the basis of both the education and the preservation of our powers of speech and song, that there is no longer any warranty for vagueness or indecision in the matter. Vocal education is thus brought out of the region of mystery, and made plain and straightforward, I would even say obvious, and quite within the powers of understanding of anyone who will take the trouble to learn what the voice really is, and what the science of phonology can practically demonstrate.